OF SOCIETIES AND MEN

CARYL P. HASKINS

With an Introduction by
VANNEVAR BUSH

Of

Societies and Men

Of

Societies and Men

NEW YORK

THE VIKING PRESS

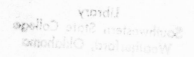

To E . F . H .

By whom this book was made.

CONTENTS

INTRODUCTION

A GREAT portion of the history of the Western world has been written in a struggle against tyranny in its many and varying forms, tyranny expressed in brutal reality when that was practicable, or in subtle dialectic when the time for brutality was not yet ripe. In this twentieth century, such tyranny is still with us. It is indeed the supreme challenge of our time. In Soviet Russia, no less than in Nazi Germany, a tyranny has been clothed in an elaborate ideology in which synthetic "communal objectives" are couched in terms for which a whole people is arbitrarily assumed to be striving. Behind this glittering façade of generalities, a tightly organized minority consolidates its ever more ruthless power and perpetuates its own ascendancy.

Leninists and Stalinists today profess to believe that man and his evolution, individual and social, have no relation to the rest of nature. Man, they will say, is a special creation, so different from the rest of nature that nothing can be argued or reasoned concerning him from all the rest of the world in which he lives. This view, of course, is one of pure mysticism. It is far from original with communism. Indeed, it is borrowed directly from the context of some of the most ancient beliefs, and represents an archaism rather than an advance in man's understanding of himself. But it contrasts strangely with that dialectical materialism of Marx of which Leninists and Stalinists profess to be the heritors and of which their social philosophy and practice, so they claim, are the embodiment. Not long ago, when these philosophers actually were materialists of a sort, they argued quite differently. Then they reasoned directly from nature, and claimed that the totalitarian way found its exemplification and its justification in certain societies of the living world which had been the most successful of all—the tightly knit, highly integrated communities of such organisms as the social insects.

This book examines both of these views, which, though directly opposed, have both been embraced at various times in the totalitarian philosophy. It searchingly considers some of the social problems of man against the timeless setting of the individual and social evolution of the whole pageant of life about him.

This is not a scientific book—although it rests upon scientific data. It is a book intended primarily for the layman. Its method, therefore, is illustrative rather than analytical, that of analogy rather than of formulation. Indeed, it depends upon analogies throughout much of its substance. Within their context these analogies may serve to illustrate the closeness of the ties that often link the social problems of man with those of the non-human living world about him—ties which inhere in the grand unity of the selectional process among all living things.

Because this is not an exhaustive treatment, it is inevitable that the material for illustration should be both limited and selected. Such selection and such limitation, though they narrow the scope of a treatment which might otherwise be much longer, do not affect its validity.

This book is of great importance to us all. It is a book of authority. Its author is at once a scientist of highest distinction in the exact study of living beings—biology—and a social philosopher who, through combining unremitting work in his special field with widely ranging participation in the affairs of the world from business operations to public service of many kinds, has laid a sound basis for an understanding of the motives and aspirations of his fellows. Few men are so well qualified as he to write with penetration and comprehension about this topic. This is, moreover, a

realistic book; the pitfalls of sentimentality and of wishful thinking do not trap us as we read it. And, as the thoughtful reader
will gladly find, it is a book of heartening confidence.

VANNEVAR BUSH

PREFACE

I N a book of this kind, it becomes almost impossible to give adequate acknowledgment to all the source-springs which have formed its basis and its inspiration. Those to which the author has consciously turned are too multifarious and varied to be fully enumerated, and there are many others to which he is deeply indebted but of which he is perhaps not even explicitly aware. A general bibliography is appended, in which an effort is made to acknowledge some of the principal materials upon which the book rests. But, inevitably, it must be considered more in the nature of a source list for those who may be interested in further and more detailed reading than as any complete portrayal of the existing store of knowledge and discovery upon which anyone interested in the subject of societies may draw.

To certain friends, however, the author's debt is both great and specific. First of all, to Dr. Vannevar Bush, without whose insistent encouragement and keen criticism through the seven years that the book was in the making it might possibly never have been completed. Then to Franklin S. Cooper and Frederick G. Fassett, Jr., from whom not only inspiration but important aspects of the philosophical approach have been drawn. To John W. Gardner, Theodosius Dobzhansky, and Lawrence Hunt, whose keen interest, generous labor, and critical approach in reviewing the manuscript exceeded the deserts of any author. To Paul A. Zahl, who provided certain of the most interesting examples of integrated societies, and supplied many comments on form and plan over the years. To my secretary, Mrs. John C. B. Hawkes, whose advice and suggestions have been much valued and whose care in preparing the manuscript is most deeply appreciated. To Dudley C. Lunt, who gave most generously of time and effort in reshaping the manuscript toward publishable form. And finally, to the staff of W. W. Norton for their consistent kindness and helpfulness in making the book a reality.

While the contributions made by these friends have been great, both for the substance and for the form of the book, its approach, its philosophy, and its point of view are those of the author, and responsibility for errors or omissions must be mine alone.

Anyone who undertakes to write of societies must feel that in so doing he essays a great adventure—one fraught with perils as well as spiced with rewards. The dangers of anthropomorphism and of false analogy beset the way. But if these can be avoided, there is the chance of achieving a somewhat wider and more inclusive viewpoint of the social way and of how it came to be. If any new vistas in the great social kingdom in which we dwell be opened to the reader of this book, if a bit of the excitement that attended its writing survive for him, then writing it will have been more than worth while.

CARYL P. HASKINS

Of
Societies and Men

CHAPTER 1

Man Against His Background

THERE ARE suggestive resemblances between the evolution of human society and that of other social organizations of the world. Some of these resemblances are superficial. Others are deceptive. But many are more than fortuitous. Their significance is the result of parallel evolution, and of the pressure of a basically similar environment upon man, who does not differ fundamentally in his constitution from the rest of the life of the earth. The significance of these relationships—the theme of this book—does not lie in the fact that man and the social insects, for instance, are directly related. Rather, it is comprehended in a grander and more inclusive conjecture.

If many social forms which are only distantly related evolve similarly under a particular set of conditions, a study of these parallels should reflect something about the environment itself. From this knowledge it may be possible to predict from the behavior of older social organisms something of the way that the society of mankind is likely to behave in the future. The assumption basic to this is that, much as the societies of man and man himself may differ from the rest of the living world in many striking features of constitution and behavior, they are none the less fundamentally similar.

In the turbulence of our modern world, with its ever-accelerating tempo of action, its ever-growing complexity of material problems, and its perpetual conflict of patterns of living, it is becoming increasingly difficult to penetrate far enough beneath the surface of our social life to detect any broad trends and any consistent patterns by which we may orient our thinking. Every material change which blesses or plagues us, every new system of ideas that arrests us, every new political or economic challenge of which we become dimly or acutely aware adds to the difficulty. We struggle in a whirlpool—in the crossrips of inconsistent and often conflicting social requirements, all of which seem equally demanding.

The profound confusion inevitably induced by conflicting demands runs to the very base of our society. It can be met only when we have learned to meet and appreciate the more basic of these conflicts. This we cannot hope to achieve in the apathy of blind acceptance, nor in the defeatism of myopic acquiescence which seeks to isolate narrow fragments of the great social framework of mankind. Peace and strength may grow through even an uncertain discernment of the misty outlines of the social country in which we live—its highest mountain ranges, its greatest rivers, and its widest plains. In the heat of the day, in the burden of the road, in the welter of the market place, in conflict and in daily toil, it comes as a bit of a shock to reflect that the human civilization in which we are so inextricably enmeshed has not been a permanent feature of the earth's development.

A most striking feature marking the contrast between the evolution of man and that of other social creatures is the extraordinary youth of *Homo sapiens* as a biological species. A corollary to this is the extraordinary dynamism of man's social development. This has an important bearing upon the whole character of human society. The most ancient paleontological indications of relatively modern types of man come predominantly, not through his fossilized bones, but through his craftsmanship. Among the earliest relics of human handiwork are the unformed eolithic stone chips of pre-Chellean workmen, picked up as they were found or fashioned by dashing one stone against another. These archaic evidences of the individual and social life of mankind were probably dropped and forgotten by their owners but a scant million years before our time. The fossilized remains of Java and Pekin man, which ordinarily are considered as representing the very archetypes of mankind, are apparently only about 650,000 years of age, while Mousterian man, including the Neanderthal of Europe, seems to have flourished only about a quarter of a million years ago. Our own Paleolithic European ancestors—the Cro-Magnons —lived and worked in Europe as late as 25,000 B.C. It seems a safe assumption that modern man appeared on earth as a dominant species little more than a million years ago, and that he entered the early phase of communal evolution at about this same time.

Compare this picture with that of the evolution of the social insects. To be conservative, the ants may be selected for this comparison. They represent one of the more recently evolved social insects—*parvenus*, as far as can be judged from their structure, compared to such ancient groups as the termites. Yet fossil ants, preserved in such condition that they can be profitably examined and reliably classified, are known from geological formations of Eocene time, about fifty million years ago. These ants are physically as modern in type, so far as can be told, as the most advanced ants of the present day. They are much more highly specialized than a great number of living forms now dwelling in remote corners of the globe in societies which are reasonably well organized and rather elaborate. These Eocene ants had already undergone specialization into social castes, and there seems good reason to conclude that their communities, far from being subsocial like those of pre-Chellean man, were already large, well integrated, and of complex constitution.

In terms of human evolution, this was the period when the earlier mammalian stocks were just becoming differentiated into the forms which were to give rise to the living orders of mammals. Among them were the remote ancestors of anthropoid apes and of men. Ages were to pass before even the more advanced types of primates, much less the most elementary forms of men, were to appear on earth. Yet at that time the ants had already reached such a high stage in their social evolution that they have since advanced or retrogressed from it only in detail. Both the individual and the social evolution of ants had been brought to essentially their present state at a period so remote that the time which has elapsed since has been fifty times as long as the period required for the entire individual and social evolution of mankind.

So with all our complexities and difficulties, we are newcomers indeed to this earth on which we dwell. But this shortness of our history, this infancy of man as a social animal, has further and more serious implications than those of mere contrast to the spectacle of the immensity of our modern society. Other social beings, myriad in number and character, have been here before us far into the dimmest reaches of geological history. Many of them have persisted, to live with us today as ancient wizened contemporaries. In their agelong development many mistakes in social evolution have been made—many blind alleys have been followed. These are suggestive and instructive. For similar social blind alleys— similar social mistakes—may threaten us today.

The problem goes further. It is quite possible that in looking at these ancient social organizations of living things as they appear today, in comparing and contrasting them among themselves and with our own society, we can discern among the many dissimilarities some underlying conformities. These latter may correspond to certain basic conditions of social life which all earthly societies of all time have been called upon to fulfill, and which we—no less than they—must obey. In our discernment of such factors, we shall have had our first glimpse of the mountain ranges, the rivers, and the plains of that "social continent" to which man the social animal, no less than his predecessors, is called upon to adapt himself successfully. Such a view may help us in gaining that wider and more comprehensive vision of our own social structure which all of us so desperately seek.

There are few indeed who have not at some time been fasci-
nated by animal societies. The hive of bees that inspired Maeterlinck, the colony of ants that absorbed the attention of Solomon
and Thoreau, the packs of the red dholes of India so vividly described by Kipling, have a lure that is unmistakable. There is something about the spectacle of a flock of wheeling pigeons, a swarm
of migrating Monarch butterflies or a colony of beavers or of
prairie marmots, something about the ordered, hushed, intensive
dynamism of a huge colony of termites, that compels attention and
demands investigation. The reason perhaps is that we are witness
to one, and possibly the most obvious, expression of a trend that is
well-nigh universal throughout nature and to which we ourselves
are subject in the highest degree—the trend of socialization. Or
perhaps it is because such societies remind us of the often basically
similar but far more complex situations with which we ourselves
are faced, never more acutely in the history of man than at the
present moment.

In time, as one compares the living societies of the world,
certain impressions occur and recur and will not be denied. It becomes imperative to seek some integrative concepts which will
unify them, will give them a rational basis, and will make them
applicable to the realm of human affairs. The most vivid of these
impressions is that of a basic underlying similarity among many
societies of the world. The most bizarre and the most divergent
sorts of living things are committed to the role of social living. Yet
above the vast differences which separate them, beyond the immense gap between the instinct pattern of the bee and the intellect
of man, beyond the immense divergencies of structure and of
evolutionary history which distinguish the various social animals,
there is a deep-laid uniformity of social behavior. The longer one
contemplates it, the more striking it becomes. Clearly, man is not
alone in his social problems and dilemmas. In one form or another,
they affect all the social life of the earth.

The purpose of this book is to explore some of the great

features of this "social continent" on which we dwell, sharing it as we do with many other social creatures and, indeed, with all the life of the earth. This exploration must necessarily be wide and general. Yet if thereby the social problem of man can be set in a broader and more unifying perspective—if the groundwork can be laid for a fresher and broader approach—the adventure will be at once exciting and worth while.

To explore that social milieu, and to examine the societies of men in this perspective, it will be necessary to bring a vast array of seemingly different things into consideration. It will be necessary to borrow from a great range of scientific disciplines, some of which are not ordinarily considered in conjunction. Repeated reference will be made to the concepts of evolution—not only in the classical sense in which that great theory was formulated by Charles Darwin and Alfred Wallace, but in some of its more detailed and subtle aspects which have been elaborated by their modern successors. We must draw on the geology of Darwin's day —on Lyell, Darwin's contemporary, and on many successors from Darwin's time to our own, for part of the evidence. We must use the paleontology of Agassiz and his predecessors and successors, to help the story. Genetics—the genetics of Mendel and De Vries, and of the most modern contemporary investigators—will be needed to help in constructing the picture. Organic chemistry, and even astrophysics, will here and there be required. And finally, there is need of sociology and psychology—the insect sociology of Fabre and Maeterlinck, of Forel and Wheeler, and of their modern spiritual descendants, and the human and comparative psychology of a host of modern workers, as a source of the needed evidence.

The task is to provide suggestive evidence, to indicate the outlines, to discern the mountain range on the horizon rather than to map it accurately. We seek to understand something of the broad framework of human society in terms of the societies which have gone before it and in terms of the natural environment amid which we dwell. The effort is to determine trends of similarity, and to discern essential differences, between the society of men and those of other social organisms of the world. Inevitably, then, this must be a book of analogies, comparisons, and contrasts drawn often between societies and creatures which may at first seem but remotely connected.

It is striking to reflect that the wide diversity of life on earth can be chemically and physiologically interpreted in remarkably uniform terms. To be sure, the variations on the main biochemical themes are enormous and they involve many elements and countless differences of combination and of reaction timing. Moreover, the raw materials potentially available on earth to life have never been fully utilized by it. But never, even in the most bizarre organisms that have been investigated, has a theoretically fundamental departure from a characteristic basic physiological theme been found. In this sense, the unity of behavior in all life is so great that it is not unreasonable to assume that the formation of a particular biological product, no matter what organism elaborates it, has proceeded through fundamentally similar steps. Life has not been so very original throughout the whole of its development.

If this is true at the biochemical level—which is the most basic to living things—it is a reasonable assumption that this fundamental similarity will be generally reflected in parallel developments of grosser characteristics over a wide range of life and its societies—for at the root, of course, these derived characteristics must have a biochemical basis. It would be reasonable to seek similarities of structure, of individual behavior, and of evolutionary trends among forms of life which appear on the surface to be very different.

In practice, we actually find that living creatures do not need to be directly related to have evolved in significantly parallel lines. It is enough that they are similar in deep-laid biochemical ways, and that they have evolved under similar environmental conditions. In such cases, the parallelism of evolution points more clearly to a particular characteristic of the *environment* than it does to the closeness of biological relationship of the evolving lines. It is to this characterization of the environment by the evolutionary trends of the creatures which have evolved in it that particular attention will be given throughout this book.

This, be it noted, is not to imply that the evolution of societies or of living things in general is controlled by environmental conditions in any such sense as that conceived by Lamarck or by recent Russian genetic theories centering about the names of Michurin or Lysenko. It has no relation to this idea, which has never been satisfactorily demonstrated. What *is* meant is that the *selection* of various mutations in evolving lines of plants and animals under similar environmental conditions is often such as to give their directions of evolution a very similar, though parallel, cast—a parallelism which may be significant and instructive in projecting the direction which evolution is likely to take in a given environment in the future.

This is a somewhat unusual standpoint from which to view the phenomena of organic or social evolution. It is more usual to stress the relationships of organisms than it is to notice the relationships of environments, or to hazard the effects that they may have in future upon other creatures from the effects which they have had in the past. Yet such a viewpoint may be quite rewarding.

In adopting this broad postulate of the basic unity of social life as a working hypothesis, it becomes extremely important to limit and define most carefully the concepts used, and to weigh most deliberately the exact degree of kinship involved in any two evolving lines. Often they are remote. Thus when various aspects of the lives of single-celled organisms, of many-celled creatures, and of societies are compared, these comparisons are to be understood as analogies only, and as limited analogies, drawn only for special purposes. It must be understood that they are to be handled with great care. *They must not be pushed too far, for they are only parallel developments, not directly connected in evolution save*

through the broad pattern of similarity which has been discussed.
The comparisons will be true in the parts that are considered.
Beyond this point, however, no assumptions can be made without
further evidence. But the limited senses in which these comparisons will be drawn can nevertheless prove remarkably illuminating concerning the nature of the environment and its significance for organic and social evolution as we know it. And this
is the environment in which our own social evolution too has
taken place.

To illustrate—the wings of a bird, of a bat, and of a pterodactyl
are actually quite different structures. In the case of the bird, the
terminal bones of the primitive vertebrate "hand" were reduced
in evolution, and feathers came to supply support; with the
bat, four of the digits were greatly elongated into supporting
"ribs" with a skin webbing between them; in the pterodactyl, only
the fourth digit was developed as a bony support for the skin wing,
ultimately reaching the fantastic length which permitted the
twenty-foot wingspread of the giant soaring *Pteranodon.* It would
be utterly fatuous to assume that these divergent structures were
directly connected with each other in evolution. But the important
fact is that all of them were wings, and all of them bore a remarkable functional resemblance in their general shape and structure.
All three, in short, were adapted to the essentially similar task of
maintaining their owners in a light gaseous medium. The physical
requirements that this condition imposed were met by suggestively
similar, though entirely parallel, modifications.

In like manner the fins and tails of fishes and of whales and the
flippers of turtles, penguins, and seals are remarkably alike at the
functional level, not because such creatures were at all directly
related in evolution—which they certainly were not—but because
these organs were constructed of basically similar biological
materials, and had the same kind of job to do in promoting the
survival of their owners in a watery medium. So wings define a
relationship of many creatures to the air, whereas flippers and
tails denote another relationship between large animals and the

water. By studying the likenesses, as well as the dissimilarities, between different kinds of wings and different kinds of fins, much may be learned about the conditions which define the directions of evolution of the vertebrates that fly or swim.

So it is with the evolution of societies. The primary purpose of this book is to discern some of the conditions which, like air or water, limit the evolution and development of societies, and using the method of comparison and analogy, to delineate their characteristics. These comparisons must be made carefully and justly, neither pushing analogies to anthropomorphism, nor mistaking the metaphor for the reality, nor, conversely, neglecting similarities that may have real significance. Man is a unique being on earth, and his evolution has been different in many ways from that of any other creature that has ever lived. So there are strict limits within which analogies from other parts of nature can apply to man and his societies. But it must be remembered too that physically man is basically an animal, subject to the same laws as the rest of life, and that many of the pitfalls which other societies have encountered in their evolution are there too for the society of man. It is a delicate task—this outlining a social continent—but an exciting one withal.

We have seen that as a biological species man is extraordinarily youthful. He is also by far the youngest social animal on earth. The youth of his social development is illumined by the time required for his social evolution when viewed in its cultural aspects. Human civilizations belong to remarkably recent times. The most remote period of ancient Egypt for which any considerable body of evidence remains is that of the First Dynasty, albeit pottery ware and figurines of ivory and clay are known from somewhat earlier times. The First Dynasty is thought to have spanned the years from approximately 3200 to 3000 B.C., while the pre-Dynastic remains are believed to date about four thousand years before Christ. An ancient calendar is known which is thought to record the years from about 4241 to 4238 B.C. It is clear that the Egyptians had passed out of the Neolithic period into what would be called a civilized state by 4000 B.C. On the conservative side this date may be extended to as early a time as 5000 B.C.

Northward of Egypt, the archaic Aegean civilization of the first Minoan period—the oldest known precursor of the civilizations of Crete and the Doric peninsula—probably flourished about 3400–2800 B.C. In the ancient flood plains of the Tigris and the Euphrates, the prehistoric ancestor-societies of the Sumerians certainly used metal, possessed manufactured pottery, and had invented writing as early as 3500 B.C. Sedimentation measurements made about their ancient seaport town of Eridu indicate that this citadel has probably been in existence approximately six thousand years.

A period seven thousand years before Christ will include the birth of the Egyptaic and Sumerian cultures. It will probably also include the Minoan and the Sinic. It far antedates the beginnings of any New World culture for which evidence has so far been discovered. Such a period, in fact, will probably encompass the beginnings of the oldest known human cultures. If, to be conservative, we add another thousand years to this span, it can then be safely said that human culture as we know it is at most but ten thousand years old.

The short evolutionary development of man, as contrasted with other forms of life, is a significant fact. In terms of life and of society on this planet, man is a *parvenu* indeed. Apart from his recorded history, the evidence of his first association with his kind dates from about a hundred thousand years ago. As a biological species, according to fossil evidence, man in approximately his present form has tenanted the earth for about a million years. This figure, which comprises a hundred times the span of his cultural evolution, is an impressive one. But compare it with the record of life on this planet. The earliest single cell is believed to have come into being about *two thousand million* years ago. Non-human multicellular life has been on earth for perhaps one-fourth as long. Societies of ants, one of the younger of the social insects, have inhabited the globe for perhaps fifty million years. What wonder, then, that the counterparts of certain trends that are only evanescent in human societies may be found greatly emphasized and more readily observed in various other living things?

What can be learned from these ancient societies that may be applicable to the problems of that youngest society of all—the society of man? In the quest for answers, a wide background must first be considered. That background includes the broad features of the stream of evolution wherein all organic life must take its course.

CHAPTER 2

The Tide to Complexity

A TIDE TO complexity in evolution is the first grand feature of the social environment which we shall seek to explore. This tide extends far beyond the domain of societies into the evolution of life itself—perhaps even into the evolution of the non-living environment of the earth. In one sense it is so simple as to appear self-evident. Yet its consequences are profound—so profound for the whole picture of social living that it demands consideration. For it dominates all earthly life and the societies formed from life, including those of men.

Since the time of Lyell paleontological research has yielded dramatic evidence that in the evolutionary development of living matter there has been an unmistakable broad trend from the simple to the complex. Both the variety of life on earth and the intricacy of its organization reflect and emphasize this trend.

The record of ancient life which paleontologists have laid bare in the rocks goes back for perhaps two thousand million years in the life of the earth. The earliest known fossils definitely indicating the presence of life on earth are probably the so-called "water biscuits." These are rounded and flattened calcareous masses, believed to have been composed of colonies of microscopic lime-secreting algae. Similar algae grow today in various parts of the world, and thus much is known of their properties and organization. They are among the simplest forms of living things. The ancient clusters in which they grew evidently represented unspecialized masses of single cells. Such fossils have been found in rocks of the enormously archaic Keewatin period and are believed to be about fifteen hundred million years old.

It is almost certain that these lime-secreting algae were by no means the only living things on earth in their day. It is highly probable that with them existed other algae, molds, bacteria, and perhaps an abundance of similarly lowly organized living things, of which no record survives because, unlike the calcified algae, they left no parts large enough or durable enough to be recorded. But it is significant that in that early time there apparently were no organisms more complex than the lime-secreting algae to leave a record in the rocks. There seems to have been nothing corresponding to the myriad forms of simpler multicellular life—sponges, clams, or snails—which are to be found in such abundance among fossils of a later time.

For more than fifty years paleontologists have carried forward an exhaustive search for evidences of more complex life in the pre-Cambrian rocks. The results have been negligible. Some marks have been discovered which may have been the trails or burrows of very simple animals. Some needles have been found in the Grand Canyon which may have been sponge spicules, though this is very uncertain. But that is all. Not even a shell exists to break the monotony of the meager record of early pre-Cambrian times. The conclusion must be that in the infancy of earthly life, the only forms that existed were too simple and too perishable to leave any record in the rocks—except in such rare cases as that of the elementary lime-secreting algae.

Beginning with the Cambrian period, about five hundred million years ago, there occurs a most dramatic change. Suddenly, as it were, the paleontologist is confronted with a magnificent fossil record of multicellular life. It is abundant in variety and fairly highly organized, though it by no means reflects the intricacy and complexity of organization of the higher life of the present day. There are fossil trilobites in abundance. There are marine shrimps, brachiopods, sponges, worms, jellyfish, snails, and possibly even primitive octopus-like creatures and other typical lowly animals of modern seas, as well as quite large seaweeds. These were immensely complex forms by comparison with the simple and meager fauna of the earlier, pre-Cambrian, years, and so great was their abundance and variety that the Cambrian strata of North America alone have yielded fossils of more than eleven hundred different kinds of animals. Both in variety and in complexity of organization, life had advanced enormously in the thirteen hundred million years or so that separated early pre-Cambrian from Cambrian time.

Yet even in the Cambrian there is no geological evidence of any terrestrial life on earth. All of the aquatic forms of that period, moreover, belong to groups which are viewed today as primitive and simple in organization in comparison with higher modern terrestrial organisms, however exquisitely specialized many of them may have been. It is not until Ordovician times, eighty million years or more after the beginning of the Cambrian, that the first vertebrates seem to have appeared as primitive, flattened, armored creatures related to the modern hagfishes. Fifty million or more additional years of earth history were to pass before specimens of the first terrestrial life were preserved, in the form of fragments of stems and bract-like leaves of what appear to have been pioneer types of land-living, semi-woody plants. Not until the Devonian period—about three hundred million years ago—were there recognizable fishes, in the form of sharks and lungfishes. Only at the close of this era did the first amphibians emerge from the slime to try their primitive and feeble limbs on land.

So it is with the entire record of the rocks, now so well documented that the evidence is virtually incontrovertible. The oldest remains of reptiles have been found in rocks of Pennsylvanian strata, laid down about two hundred and fifty million years ago. It was at this time too that insects apparently first appeared, and seed-ferns, scouring-rushes, and scale trees emerged. Not until Jurassic times, possibly less than one hundred and fifty million years ago, was the earliest record of reptilian toothed birds left in the rocks. The first archaic mammals—unimpressive, possibly shrewlike creatures—seem to have appeared about the same time. Only in the recent record of the Pliocene formations, little more than a million years old, is there recognizable evidence of any truly manlike ancestor of the human race.

On such a record there can be little question that for the last fifteen hundred to two thousand million years life on earth has evolved in such a manner as tremendously to increase its abundance and variety as well as to elaborate the intricacy of individual organisms themselves. Life has constantly been making of our planet a more and more bewilderingly complex system. Now, it is interesting that evidence of this tendency to build complex from simpler living organizations can also be found in the social evolution of various of the communal creatures of earth. This may be of the highest significance.

Take the termites, for instance. Fossil termites have been found in European and North American deposits the oldest of which date back fifty million years or so. It was a time when the mammals were evolving rapidly but the great apes had probably not yet appeared. Man was still far distant from the scene.

Virtually all of these termites belonged to genera a few members of which still survive in the world, or to groups closely related though now extinct. Most of these living genera today form relatively simple communities, consisting of only three castes, the queens, the kings, and the soldiers, together with some immature soldier forms which resemble, but are not, true workers.

Contrast this simplicity with the communities of the most highly evolved modern termites living in Africa and Australia. Millions of inhabitants may compose a single colony. They dwell in nests sometimes eighteen to twenty feet tall. As many as eight distinct castes and sixteen different classes of individuals make up such a community, all centering about a single queen. This queen may attain as much as twenty thousand times the body volume of a worker and may lay perhaps as many as sixty million eggs during her life span of ten years or so! Thus the termite colony, as an entity, appears to have increased hugely in actual size and in complexity during its evolution. It has repeated in miniature the experience so common in the whole organic world.

The same increase of complexity is conspicuously true of the societies of ants. Many fossil ants are known. The impressions of those from the Baltic and Sicilian ambers—where they were trapped in Oligocene and Miocene times in the sticky resinous sap of ancient forests—are as perfectly preserved as though they had been mounted yesterday. Among the most prominent of these amber ants are genera such as *Prionomyrmex* which are of exceedingly generalized bodily structure. This genus is extinct today, but it is clear that it is closely related to a whole group of extraordinary living ants peculiar to Australia and the surrounding areas. They are believed to represent one of the most ancient living expressions of communal life among the Formicidae.

All of these archaic ants form small and simple communities, rarely comprising more than a thousand individuals, while in many species a community may include not more than two or three dozen members. Only three castes are represented—the male, the queen, and the workers. The latter two classes are often so slightly differentiated that a careful examination is necessary to distinguish between them. Compare this simplicity with the complexity of a colony of one of the modern fungus-growing ants such as *Atta cephalotes* of tropical America, the nests of which may include as much earth as a small cottage. Here the communities consist of many thousands of individuals and include, in addition to the males and queens, a dozen or more types of workers which range in size from almost the stature of the queen to a creature so tiny that it can ride on a queen's antenna and scarcely be noticed. Once again, the tide to complexity in social evolution.

The societies of man have, of course, been conspicuously subject to this same trend. What Neanderthaloid community, what Aurignacian village, what Persian city of only twenty thousand years ago, could compare, on the basis of the fairly full evidence available, with the complexity even of a small town of today? From time immemorial man, in all his modes and aspects of living, has also followed this path from the simple to the complex. Ever since the day when his society was no more than a semi-hostile family group, he has striven with all his might to expand, step by step, first his individual life and then that of his group, until village communities arose from families and villages became city-states. It would seem, too, that throughout he has realized, in a half-conscious but deeply poignant way, the character and direction of this great slow tide of evolution. As long as we have knowledge of his folkways he has resisted the trends which would obviously oppose that tide and would force a retreat from complexity back to a more simple state, though in truth in more subtle ways he has sometimes lost that battle.

This is the evidence of the march to complexity derived from paleontology and from social evolution. Another source of evidence, in many ways quite as rich, although more presumptive, is the so-called phenomenon of *recapitulation*. This is the term for the repeated observation that throughout the world of organic life, plants and animals tend to suggest in phases of their individual growth parts of the evolutionary history of their races, though the coincidence is usually far from perfect. Thus the human embryo proceeds through stages remarkable in their similarity to corresponding growth-phases of much lower organisms of the general class from which mankind is believed to have arisen. Similarly the young larva of the crab may resemble the adult forms of much simpler types of Crustacea. Although it is rare that the early development of an organism precisely recaptures elements of the history of its race, the similarities are often highly suggestive in their broader reaches.

This condition is as true of societies as it is of individual organisms. Thus the young colony of the social stinging insects—the ants, the bees, and the wasps—is typically started by a single individual female. This founding queen represents the archetype of the species. She is the seed of the plant that is to grow. Until her first progeny has matured, the colony is at its very simplest, reflecting the presocial situation among the stinging insects.

The higher fungus-growing ants—such as *Atta cephalotes*—provide good examples of the steady trend toward complexity which characterizes the growth of the individual colony and, it is believed, mirrors the general course of ant societies in their evolution. The young female *Atta* is a relatively huge insect. She has wings and is endowed with the full gamut of instincts of the species. On a given day she emerges from her parent colony, accompanied by a group of young sister queens and crowds of males, and attended by swarms of worker personnel especially marshaled for this occasion. After a bit of hesitation, the young queen mounts a twig or a stone and takes off.

Briefly she soars and mates in flight. Upon her descent she detaches her own wings, and runs rapidly over the ground seeking a suitable niche, where forthwith she begins to dig. Excavating a passage, she enlarges it at the end to form a brood chamber, and promptly closes herself off from the outside world. Next she ejects from an inner recess of her mouth a pellet of refuse well filled with threads of fungus—garnered earlier from the gardens of her parent colony. Within a few days these threads proliferate and the queen gathers them into a compact mass and begins to cultivate the new garden assiduously. Upon this fungus garden the colony will later depend for its subsistence. Shortly the queen lays a few eggs, and as these hatch the minute larvae are carefully reared by their mother. They grow rapidly and change to pupae (chrysalids) prematurely, soon to emerge as tiny workers—the smallest, or nearly the smallest, caste known for the species. These pallid dwarfs break a passage out of the sealed chamber, timidly explore the outer world, and harvest and bring in a few leaves and other bits of vegetable matter to nourish the growing fungus garden. So well developed has this garden now become that the queen is able to take some food from it. Forthwith she lays additional eggs, and these are promptly adopted and cared for by the young workers.

Henceforth the queen will take less and less interest in the growing brood and will gradually specialize in laying until, at the maturity of the colony, her egg production will reach an immense figure. In the meantime, the second brood of young workers, cared for by their older nest mates, matures, attaining to somewhat larger stature. In the third or fourth brood the first hint of a new and larger worker caste may appear. Thereafter, as the colony increases in size, additional castes make their appearance and begin to specialize as soldiers, leaf gatherers, or guards, or in the constant weeding and care of the fungus garden. At last, when the whole gamut of the worker caste is represented and the colony is mature, new young queens and males appear. The cycle is complete. All the castes of the species are represented. The colony numbers many thousands. The maximum of complexity has been reached.

The communities of many wasps and bees go through a similar growth cycle—the honeybee is atypical in this respect—while colonies of termites are usually started in much the same fashion by an original male and female—the royal pair—working in cooperation. It is a rehearsal, in a season or in one, two, or five years, of an evolutionary development that has clearly required for its completion the fifty million years or so since Tertiary time.

This tide from simplicity to complexity which so vitally affects all social creatures, including man, may be far older than life itself. It may even be more fundamental in character than organic evolution as we understand it today. In the molecular realm, indeed, it may well be characteristic of the transition of a hot to a cool planet, such as may have occurred in the evolution of the earth and of our neighboring solar satellites—Jupiter, Venus, and Mars. Thus the laws which govern the behavior of ideal gases are widely applicable to studies of the hot stars. By contrast, the situation is far different in the cool planets. Here the chemical elements, so characteristically uncombined in the hot stars, have been aggregated into simple compounds. These in turn have been transformed into larger complexes of infinite range and variety. Liquids of a great range of composition now abound, and various kinds of solutions, suspensions, and crystalline and non-crystalline solids have made their appearance. The channels for the physical and chemical rearrangement of matter have become as branched and tortuous as the delta of a great river.

Thus on the non-living level there is reason to suppose that a trend to complexity has been characteristic of the evolution of the solar planets and has been carried to unprecedented heights in our own earth. The formation of chemical compounds appears to have occurred to a limited extent in the sun. Molecular carbon, methene, and cyanogen have all been detected in the solar spectrum, together with the oxides of a number of metals. If we accept the conclusion drawn by many scientists that the earth and its sister planets were derived from the material of the sun, then it follows that such light and simple chemical compounds were probably included in their original inheritance. Unless the planets were built up of important quantities of cold planetesimal matter, it seems probable that these were the most complex compounds included in the early substance of the young hot planets. Yet it seems clear that most if not all of the solar planets contain within their substance today much more complex chemical compounds.

The degree to which this trend to complexity has proceeded in the evolution of the planets and the details of its course have differed markedly from world to world in accordance with differing local situations. At least two peculiar conditions on the surface of the earth seem to have favored the spectacular trend to complexity which we see exemplified in the evolution even of the non-living chemical substances of our planet. The first of these is the peculiar range of surface temperatures at present characteristic of our earth, in comparison with its sisters in the solar system. This condition is at least partially explicable in terms of the relative size of the earth and its relative distance from the sun. The second condition is the abnormal abundance of water on earth, a situation which has never been accounted for in a wholly satisfactory way. The fact of this abundance of water, coupled with the related and supremely important fact that the ambient temperatures of the globe are such as to permit of the existence of large quantities of water simultaneously in the gaseous, liquid, and solid states, has probably been of tremendous importance in promoting the complexity of the non-living world which exists about us today. The predominant importance of these two factors in permitting the origin of life and consequently of societies on earth and their subsequent trend to complexity should be doubly emphasized.

Thus there is good evidence that throughout the evolution of earthly life there has been a broad but unmistakable trend from the simple toward a more complex condition in the range, the variety, and the constitution of all life and of societies. This has also been true in many aspects of the evolution of the non-living earth. The breadth of this trend has a very distinct bearing upon the problems posed by living societies. It emphasizes the possibility that, though common to life and the societies formed from life, it may be far older and more fundamental than life itself. Life, and the societies built from life, may represent merely the culmination of this tendency.

If the basic causes of this trend to complexity are not, then, to be found primarily in the laws of organic evolution, where else shall they be sought? This is a most profound question. If a clear understanding of it were ever achieved in detail, it would immensely broaden our comprehension of the dynamics of the living world and most particularly of social evolution. But the challenge is enormous.

Under the conditions obtaining on earth, carbon, hydrogen, nitrogen, and oxygen can produce a bewildering variety of immensely complex chemical substances of a tremendous range of structure. These elements alone can provide an extremely complicated stockpile of raw materials for the building of living protoplasm. And these are but a few, albeit the principal, elements that go to make up life.

At a higher level of organization, again, a few dozen genes inherent in a single population of a single species of animal or plant could produce a vast number of variations among the individuals of that population through their fortuitous recombination. Thus the complexity of a population mixture might be immensely increased in a few generations, even if the genes were assumed to be fixed, non-varying quantities. But we know that the genes are themselves mutable, so that variety will be still further multiplied. At a yet higher level of organization, a few thousand of such varying individuals can produce exceedingly varied and complicated societies. Thus a tide to complexity, beginning among entities like the simpler, non-living organic chemical substances, must ultimately be reflected in that highest organization of all—the living society.

Probably no human mind could acquire the phenomenal knowledge or the power of analysis necessary to comprehend in detail the meaning of such an immense panorama of change and recombination in the non-living and the living worlds. But that such change will lead to great complication is evident. At the same time, the complexity and variety are aggravated by the fact that simpler entities have not ceased to exist on earth as more complex ones have appeared. Thus, free electrons and simple gases still occur on earth, together with immensely complex organic compounds. In the living realm there are bacteria, as well as elephants, and in the social field the primitive semisocial insects continue to exist side by side with the most complex and advanced insect societies.

Further, in the living realm the tide to complexity may often be reversed, and may become a trend to simplification and specialization. This is equally true of life itself and of the societies built from life. Thus what we actually see on earth is an exceedingly delicate and intricate equilibrium between simpler and more complex entities, both among organisms and among societies. While this situation is analyzable in detail—as students of evolution are constantly doing with respect to specific parts of the theater of life —in its totality it staggers the imagination. But despite the difficulty of quantitative description there can be no doubt of its reality and universality, and there need be no mystery about the trend from simplicity to complexity.

In still other ways, more important with respect to social evolution, the trend to complexity is enormously aided and abetted by the characteristics of life itself. It is a fundamental and a most important quality of life that it tends to increase. This is a way of saying that, with the passage of time, all living things tend to transform more and more of the earth substances on which they feed into the complex chemical images of their own living structure. From this obvious yet deeply significant fact, many things follow.

Merely by increasing the *number* of living things on earth, life is constantly enhancing the complexity of our terrestrial system. Since life is inherently changeable, it universally tends to become ever-increasingly varied in form and function as it increases its range to include more and more different situations on the planet. Perhaps of greatest importance, each generation of living things, through its own action on the earth and its inhabitants, bequeaths to its descendants an environment which becomes more complex with the passing aeons, a complexity to which new life can then adjust itself. Thus by its action on the earth life accelerates its own trend to complexity.

Finally, this tendency of every form of life constantly to increase in its own image frequently leads to the formation of aggregates of living things—to emergent societies, as it were, of a new order of structure. In the course of evolution this has led, for example, to the formation of multicellular organisms from individual cells and to the rise of colonies of wasps or bees from single solitary insects. Once formed, these societies are often stable and become subject themselves to the same complicating and aggregating trends. Thus they not only grow more complex with time but may evolve aggregates of a yet higher order.

Like the evolution of life in general, the evolution of human society has exhibited a constant tendency to diverge and to give rise to ever more variant and complex types. Thus the human world, like the organic one, has tended to grow more complex and diversified since the dawn of civilization. The final surge of this trend to complexity is attained in the cultural aspects of human society. With the structure that is human culture, it achieves the peak of its power and vigor.

In human affairs there are many familiar examples of this tide to complexity. If we view man as a biological species, it is spectacularly shown in the diversity of his physical races, even within the confines of a single continent. Consider the multifarious types and tribes native to Africa or South America. Consider the extraordinary range of physical types inhabiting even so restricted an island as Great Britain.

In human culture these trends to diversity and complexity appear more vividly, and with even greater subtlety. Compare the complexity of organization of an ancient Swiss Lake village with that of modern Paris, the Anglo-Saxon hundreds and their primitive courts with modern British jurisprudence, American colonial settlements with the modern United States.

It would be hard to find a clearer example than the spread and diversification of Polynesian culture throughout the Pacific Seas. Originally the Polynesians appear to have migrated from the mainland of Asia. Traveling perhaps even then in the great sea canoes which were one of the outstanding products of their later culture, they finally came to populate the vast congeries of tiny landfalls which dotted their immense ocean kingdom, stretching from Hawaii to New Zealand, and far to the eastward to the tiny outpost of Rapa Nui off the coast of South America—the famed Easter Island.

At the height of their vigor and power, the Polynesians kept the sea lanes between their far-flung islands open, and travel between them was relatively frequent. Then as their power waned, the picture changed. After the fourteenth century, it appears that intercourse between the islands gradually died away. Thereafter each became a tiny isolated kingdom. And then it was that the great tide of diversity in human culture became most evident. For, although each of these Polynesian islands had originally been populated by closely related peoples with a generally common culture, striking and unique cultural features eventually appeared in each. Thus New Zealand is peculiarly conspicuous today for the beauty of its woodworking art, and the vivid decorations of the great wooden sea canoes are proverbially famous. Elsewhere, megalithic stone architecture and the construction of stone monuments became very characteristic of Polynesian culture. But here again the particular modes of stone working and their modeling vary so widely from island to island as to create a distinct sub-culture for every Polynesian group. In Samoa, Tonga, and Tahiti are to be found magnificent step-pyramids of stone. In the Marquesas, Rarotonga, and Pitcairn Island the art took the form of great stone temples—the *maraes*. Finally, an entirely distinct megalithic art was developed on Easter Island. Here the sculptors carved humanized forms in bold relief from the soft volcanic rock, working from niches excavated about the developing figures. When their task was nearly complete, they cut each statue away from its base and dragged it to its final site.

There was a similar diversification of language form among the Polynesians. Today the Polynesian language is split into at least eight well-marked variants—the Samoan, Maori, Tahitian, Hawaiian, Tongan, Managarevan, the Nukuhivan of the Marquesas, and the language of the Paumoto Archipelago. Finally, while writing seems to have been unknown in most of ancient Polynesia, wooden tablets found on Easter Island contain a unique and complex ideographic script.

These are but the simplest and most generalized of examples, and they are taken from the most elementary setting of one primitive culture. Yet even within this tiny niche of human development, the tide to complexity, even over a very few centuries, is amply evident. On a far grander scale that tide has been operative throughout the biological, the social, and the cultural evolution of mankind.

CHAPTER 3

The Drive to Integration

WHAT MAY be called a drive to integration is another great feature of the social continent which deeply affects organic and social evolution. It is the tendency both of organisms and of certain kinds of societies, evolving under the pressure of natural selection, to become more and more close-knit entities, and of their parts to become increasingly specialized and dependent upon the whole. While it co-exists with the tide to complexity, and the effects of the two are often interwoven, it is far less universal in its manifestation. Indeed, whole classes of societies fail to exhibit it. Nevertheless, it is of the highest importance. What is involved is the adjustment and welding of the parts of an inefficient and loosely organized social grouping, whereby it is transformed into a compact, smoothly operating whole. Vivid examples of this trend are to be found among animal societies. Some of the most interesting occur among the social insects.

Not all wasps and bees are social creatures. Indeed, almost nine-tenths of the known forms lead strictly solitary lives. The so-called mud daubers, for instance, so familiar in our summer woods and fields, are solitary wasps. The female constructs exquisitely fashioned cells of clay under rocks or the eaves of buildings or in other protected places. Each cell is packed with spiders, caterpillars, or similar provender, which have been sought out in their hiding places and paralyzed by the huntress. As each cell is filled, a single egg is laid, so placed that the young larva which hatches from it will be within easy reach of the helpless larder. Then the chamber is sealed, and the mother, after putting the finishing touches to the structure, flies off to begin a new one. These cells are widely scattered, so that much diffuse effort is required to complete and provision them. In due time, the egg in each cell hatches and the larva feeds, grows, and changes to a chrysalis. Finally it emerges as a solitary winged adult to repeat the cycle.

There is nothing obviously social in this stereotyped pattern of behavior. It has apparently been repeated, with little variation, by the more primitive solitary wasps, generation by generation since perhaps Mesozoic times, seventy million or more years ago. Yet it clearly contained the seeds of the social way of life. For to the best of our knowledge it was from creatures of this general type that transitional forms arose which led ultimately to those often highly socialized insects, the colony-forming wasps, the ants, and the social bees.

One of the early steps in the direction of socialization in this evolution was the highly significant one of consolidation and integration. Instead of scattering her brood cells widely over the countryside, the mother-builder tended increasingly to construct them closer together and thus to consolidate and standardize her work. Many of the living forms of solitary wasps and bees are still in this stage of evolution. Even today certain solitary wasps tend to construct collections of mud cells, piled one atop another, or immediately adjacent. Or they may take advantage of tubular cavities in twigs, the interstices of walls, or hollows in the ground to construct a group of contiguous cells. Each cell will be provisioned with small paralyzed caterpillars and an egg, carefully suspended by a filament from the ceiling out of reach of the dangerous writhings of the prey. Among the more advanced solitary wasps and bees a further development of consolidation may take place. The walls enclosing each cell may be dispensed with and a simple partition substituted, foreshadowing the development of a comb.

Thus among some species of a rare solitary bee—*Allodape*— the founding female begins by finding or excavating a long tubular gallery in the stem of a plant. A packet of pollen and honey is made and crowded to the bottom of the nest. An egg is laid on it, but no envelope is constructed around it. A second packet is built on top of the first and another egg deposited. There follows a third, and so on until the tube is filled. The mother insect then deserts the family. Presently the eggs hatch and the larvae develop in close association, to pupate and emerge as adults at about the same time. By force of circumstance, they may live together in a group for a little while. But as they have small mutual attraction and no real mutual interest, they soon disperse. This is an early step in consolidation.

The next social advance is achieved through an interaction of the two trends toward complexity and integration so intimate that they cannot be separated. The life span of the mother becomes prolonged until she is able to survive the final emergence of her offspring. At the same time, the evolution of the brood cell may go forward in one of two ways. On the one hand, as the mother's longevity and fertility increase, the chambers become more numerous, taking on a somewhat standardized form and becoming more closely crowded together. The female ceases to provide each brood cell with a large store of nourishment. Instead she takes an increasing interest in her brood and progressively furnishes them with food as they require it. This permits the cell to be shrunken and simplified and greatly contributes to its consolidation and standardization. The ultimate product of this trend is the compact comb of the social wasp or honeybee, with its regular rows of hexagonal cells, so uniform that they seem built to a standard pattern.

It is interesting to notice that the queen brood cells of the honeybee still have a shape very different from the regular cells used for rearing other forms of brood and as storage pots for honey. Instead, they are huge baglike affairs which project conspicuously from the surface of the comb, giving mute evidence that bees, like other social organisms, may be conservative in relation to their royalty, for this form of cell is basically primitive in character.

The other direction which evolution may take is shown in a group of semisocial wasps in the Philippines known as the Stenogastrines. The shy and barely social forest wasp *Stenogaster depressigaster* illustrates the next transitional stage from solitary to social existence possibly as well as any living creature. It builds delicate little nests consisting of thin and infinitely fragile tubes made of fragments of decayed wood or particles of earth precariously cemented together, hung from the tip of a pendent fungus or fern. Each tube consists of a few intertwined and braided cells, and on each nest are usually to be found a few adult wasps. Ready to disperse at the slightest alarm, they probably constitute a small evanescent family, including the original female and such of her daughters as are not yet ready to begin life on their own and still cling to the parental homestead. This society must be precarious indeed. For with a closely related wasp, where the mother builds a very similar nest of contiguous cells, constructed of similar materials and placed in similar situations, the young disperse so quickly that this species is reckoned as a solitary one. This is the slender thread by which at its inception the existence of social life may hang!

Such a precarious aggregation could hardly persist in evolution on any large scale. It is remarkable that *Stenogaster depressigaster* still survives as a species. It is surely a relic of a very unstable condition, fortuitously preserved as a "living fossil." It would be expected that the social state among wasps and bees should be further consolidated if it were to persist at all. It is abundantly evident that this did, in fact, occur. Another stage on the road is well illustrated by the life history of the common bumblebee.

The solitary young queen of the bumblebee establishes her family in the spring in a manner not dissimilar from that of the solitary bee *Allodape*. Finding or excavating a burrow in the ground, she assembles a large mass of pollen paste and leaves it intact to form the floor of the cell. On top of this she builds a circular wall of wax, fashioned from flakes of this substance secreted by her own body. The first clutch of eggs is laid in this single cell.

Here, in contrast to the cells of *Allodape*, there are no partitions between the eggs. As soon as they are deposited the cell is covered over. Next the queen constructs a large waxen pot, placing it on the floor of the nest within easy reach of the brood cell. This storage chamber is filled with honey. The queen, resting on the top of the cell, now proceeds literally to brood the developing eggs, feeding, for the most part, from the honey store in front of her.

As the eggs hatch, the larvae begin to devour the pollen floor of their chamber. Periodically the queen bites a small hole in the waxen skin over her young and injects a little honey among them, which they greedily consume. She also replenishes the pollen supply from time to time. In about eleven days the larvae mature and each spins a cocoon under the wax. The cocoons adhere strongly side by side to form a compact mass. The mother now clears away the wax, exposing this mass of cocoons, which she continues to brood for several days.

When the cocoons are finally hatched, it becomes evident that a further important advance has been made in integrating the colony and consolidating its structure. For the young of this first brood of the bumblebee are not perfect and potentially independent daughters and sons bound to their parent by the most slender of instinctive ties, as in the more primitive semisocial wasps and bees. Instead they are females only—and imperfect females at that. Some are no larger than houseflies, and most of them are sterile, or nearly so, and thus incapable of founding new communities. What is even more important, their instinct-endowment is incomplete. Maternal instincts are highly developed, but reproductive instincts are largely absent. The whole complex of instinctive knowledge which enables every young female of a solitary species to go through the intricate patterns involved in the selection of a nesting site and in the making and provisioning of a cell are almost wholly wanting. These defective daughters must stay at home, contributing to the stability and the growth of the colony. Were they ever to leave the parental domicile permanently, they would be wholly lost.

The founding bumblebee female now gives little further attention to foraging or to the rearing of the new broods of young which successively appear. These duties are almost entirely taken over by the new workers. As the summer wears on, more and more workers are matured. They become larger in average stature as the population of the colony increases until at last, in the fall, true queens and males appear and the cycle from queen to queen, which in the *Allodape* colony requires but one brood, is at last complete.

A society has been stabilized. It has acquired a certain individuality. This social evolution has been aided by a number of factors: in *Stenogaster* by the collection of scattered individual brood cells into one place; in the bumblebee by the formation of a single brood chamber and by the welding of the first brood of daughters into a homogeneous working social unit. This last development, however, has involved a heavy sacrifice of the individual potentialities of the early broods of daughters—and indeed of the greater part of the whole population of the colony.

The further stages in the evolution of the societies of wasps and bees are familiar ones. Bit by bit, the workers become sharply differentiated and highly co-ordinated in their duties and grow increasingly dependent upon the colony for their existence. At the peak of this development in the honeybee there are nurses and sweepers, ventilators and foragers, and attendants of the queen which do little beyond their special tasks for the duration of their tours of duty, though one bee may perform several of these tasks at successive periods of its life. Bit by bit systems of communication become established. These grow in precision until co-ordination is so perfect that the colony gives the impression of acting as a single unit. Co-ordination, regulation, subordination, and discipline of the colony members—these have been the unmistakable trends.

The social insects probably mark the furthest point of this path of development among communities of many-celled creatures as we ordinarily visualize such communities. Yet the wasp or bee, termite or ant colony is actually still a comparatively loosely integrated structure. Although its members may be interdependent in action, yet any one of them can be removed and kept apart from the community for a period and then subsequently returned without damage to the part or to the whole. Although an injury dealt to any part of a colony of these social insects may ultimately be perceived and fiercely resented by the rest of the community, yet the reaction of the colony as a whole to the threat, by defense or flight, is, on the whole, slow and awkward. Perhaps the course of evolution of societies on earth is still too recent to have permitted further integrative development along the social road. Perhaps the fact that there is no permanent physical connection among the members of the insect community has inhibited or delayed the trend. Be that as it may, it is interesting to see that the integrative phase of social evolution has actually been carried much further in a more primitive class of invertebrates, where physical connections have been established among the members.

One does not ordinarily think of a jellyfish as a social creature or as one likely to embark on social development. Yet in one group of them—the Siphonophora—the social structure has attained to a higher degree of integration and individuality than in any other class of societies.

The social habit is, in fact, common among the allies of the jellyfishes. The polyps of corals and of the purple sea fans, for example, form immensely populous communities. But since they remain permanently stationary there need be little differentiation among the members of a colony. It is among the allies of the mobile jellyfish that the evolution of social life offers a most striking illustration of the drive to integration.

In the marine siphonophoran genus *Halistemma,* individual organisms associate into rather diffuse colonies in which all the members are nevertheless physically interconnected. A single colony takes the form of a long pendent string, to which various specialized structures are attached. Each structure actually represents a highly modified individual member of the community. At the top is a small float, from which hangs the slender axial fiber of the colony. Several swimming bells are attached to this fiber by strands a short distance below the float. These "bells" are members of the colony which can only swim. They possess no mouths, and must therefore be nourished through their physical connections with other, feeding, individuals of the community. But they are highly efficient swimmers, and their function is to keep the colony afloat and to move it about.

Farther down the fiber there are groups of differently specialized individuals. Some of these are hunters. Equipped with mouths and single long tentacles, they capture prey, digest it, and distribute the products through their connecting stems to the other members of the colony. In addition, there are curiously modified members which function as special protective structures, others which have no mouths but are furnished with long tentacles to act as defensive stinging equipment or as fishing lines to capture and paralyze prey, and finally mouthless and tentacleless reproductive forms. Their social function is to produce new colonies.

The manner in which the colony develops is extraordinarily interesting. From an egg produced by one of the reproductive members there hatches a small single larva. As this larva matures, it produces descendants by budding, like any solitary jellyfish. But these descendants, unlike those of the solitary forms of jellyfish, do not separate from the parent. Nor could they do so at this stage of their evolution, for they are no longer structurally self-supporting organisms. Each develops directly into a form with the characteristic specialized functions which will thereafter typify it and make of it an integral and completely dependent unit in a community. Thus the swimming bells and the fishing lines and the mouthless sexual forms are wholly dependent on the other members of the community for every requirement other than the specialized function which they themselves perform.

This is a far more highly integrated social structure than the most thoroughly specialized of insect communities. Yet it appears to be one of the most diffuse and generalized of the siphonophoran colony-organisms. In the related genus *Physophora* the bewilderingly diffuse structure of the *Halistemma* colony is much consolidated. There is still a float with a fiber hanging from it, equipped with specialized swimming bells. But below the bells the fiber is shortened. The groups of bizarre colony members have been assembled in a compact knot, and the protective individuals have been grouped as a defensive ring around them. In the genus *Stephalia* there has been further specialization and organization. The upper float is now greatly enlarged and strengthened, and the swimming bells are grouped in an orderly manner just below it. Immediately underneath this swimming equipment the rest of the colonial members lie almost fused together in a single mass. One is reminded, in all this compacting of colonial structure, of the early trend among the females of the first semisocial wasps and bees to gather together and compress their brood cells.

The gorgeous Portuguese man-of-war, trailing its yard-long fishing line as it drifts over the quiet surfaces of tropical seas, presents the culmination of this development. In this colony the individuality of the community has become so overwhelmingly predominant that it is tempting to consider the creature as a unitary organism. That is almost what it is. The greatly enlarged float, which is crested and can be deflated, has usurped the entire swimming function of the community. The now useless swimming-bell members have disappeared. Underneath the float is a group of feeding individuals with mouths but no tentacles. Associated with them, and assisting them in the capture of prey as well as in the defense of the colony, are several members bearing venomous fishing lines. Here also is attached the stupendously long line so conspicuous and so startling to human bathers. Here likewise are the reproductive members, protectively situated near the heart of the colony, from which new individuals, and thence new communities, will arise.

Among the Siphonophorans social evolution has thus come to a nearly full cycle. Integration of colony members, exquisite internal co-ordination, the genesis of a new composite "personality" in the community—all these have at last made the colony as a

THE DRIVE TO INTEGRATION

whole so like the solitary individual jellyfish from which it arose in evolution that structurally its individual members are scarcely distinguishable as such. This surely is the end of the road of social integration. It is a characteristic finale.

The history of human social evolution is not without conspicuous evidences of the influence of this social trend to integration. The League of the Five Nations of the Iroquois, with its specialization of the Onondagas to leadership of the clans, of the Senecas to the so-called doorkeeper function, and its complex political and social structure, is an example in point in a relatively primitive society. So also was that far more striking and more ambitiously integrated Indian state to the southward—the Inca of Peru, with its tightly regimented vassal states and its hereditary chieftainships and governing class. The same tendency was unusually vividly illustrated in the reorganization of Japan under the Tokugawa Shoguns, with the shrewd integration of the holdings of the barons into the greater domains of the Shogunate which followed it and the consolidation of power in the court of Iyeyasu. Such tendencies can be found equally well illustrated at many points in the evolution of the Roman Empire and in the work of Clovis and Charlemagne, of the Norman kings of England, of Garibaldi and Cavour. In many times and places this trend has persisted and has sometimes been further accentuated. We recently fought a war to halt its latest expression in the fanatic nationalisms of peoples.

It is evident that the trend to integration leads from a more diffuse to a more closely compacted social structure. It also leads to a much closer integration of these consolidated elements.

There follows a marked specialization of the individuals or organizations within this new social structure. They become at once more useful in it and less fit to live alone. At the same time the tolerance of the society for members of other integrated social structures is likely to decrease sharply. Thus with many ants the members of a single colony, though almost invariably friendly to one another, will not tolerate the entry of any stranger, even of their own species. After Portuguese men-of-war have reached full colonial development, although they travel in fleets, they do not fuse to form larger colonies. In a word, while this trend to integration and consolidation confers upon the society some of the qualities of a separate individual, at the same time the sphere of individuality of its component parts may become sharply circumscribed.

The trend to integration may confer powerful advantages upon those societies which in evolution are committed to that road. For in competition with other such integrated societies, it is the community that is the closest knit, the best co-ordinated, and the most efficient *as a whole* that must finally survive. It is this total competence of the whole society, dependent upon the specialized aptitudes of its members but quite apart from their individual overall competences, which may be critical for survival in selection of this kind. This fact is illustrated over and over again in the natural history of the social insects.

No matter how superior the members of a primitive ant colony may be as individuals, the closely co-ordinated colony of a more advanced and specialized type has a tremendous advantage over its loosely organized primitive predecessor. In Bermuda, until very recent years, there lived in abundance a socially primitive ant— *Odontomachus haematoda.* Its galleries were everywhere along the coral walls and by the coral boulders of the sunny upland meadows under the cedar trees. It is a comparatively large ant of active and athletic habit and with well-developed sense organs. But the social organization of its rather small communities, though above that of the primitive wasps, is diffuse and feeble. A number of years ago, a socially highly organized species of grain-harvesting ant— *Pheidole megacephala*—was introduced into Bermuda as a stowaway on a ship, perhaps from its original home in the East. The individual members of this colony are tiny insects, scarcely one-tenth the bulk of the native ant and physically much less well endowed. But their communities are well-organized and close-knit structures and the workers are co-ordinated to a high degree. The colonies have become efficient individual fighting units.

Confining itself at first to the salt-sprayed regions of the coral beaches, where most native ants would have perished, the invader gradually built up a ring of occupation around the island. Then, foot by foot and year by year, it narrowed the circle. Battling its way into the cedar groves and upland hills, it gradually overran the territory of the natives. It invaded their very citadels, attacking the large and courageous but individualistic workers in numbers and killing them one by one. So intense and ruthless was the battle that it was terminated only by the extermination of the natives. Today, *Odontomachus* has all but disappeared from its former haunts, and *Pheidole*, its alien competitor, is the universal occupant along the walls and beneath the boulders of the cedar-studded hills.

However rugged or self-reliant the individual Iroquois or Algonquin, Australian Bushman or Zulu, may have been—however superior in many features his sensory and mental organization—his loosely knit society has been destroyed or absorbed by the closely knit units of some dominant people whenever there has been serious competition. It seems beyond question that there is much survival value for a society in close-knit integration and organization.

This survival value may well be the key to the drive to communal integration, which is so widespread among certain kinds of societies. Hence one would expect it to have been emphasized by natural selection throughout evolution. That it has been so emphasized is obvious, but it is very important. We speak of evolution and treat it in terms of the behavior of populations, races, species. These are the effects that we see. Yet natural selection, as ordinarily understood, is based on the concept of individuality. In the last analysis, competition arises among more or less distinct individuals, and natural selection occurs between them. It is easy to imagine a biological competition for food of the most intense sort among the primitive cells which floated in the primordial waters of the world. The contents of these cells quite likely did not differ markedly in their total composition from that of the surrounding water. But each cell was enclosed by a partially permeable membrane which walled it off from its surroundings and distinguished it from other cells. Hence it functioned as a unit in competition with other units. It is not difficult to see that the system exhibiting the greatest capacity for assimilation and growth would overrun and eventually exterminate its less dynamic neighbors. But suppose, for argument, that all these cell walls had suddenly been dissolved and the contents of these primeval organisms had been released again into the oceans from which they were derived. The chemical composition of the waters as a whole might be very little altered. But a great and significant change would nevertheless have occurred. A homogeneous system would have been re-established in which all biological selection—all evolution as we know it—would cease to be a possibility. Natural selection depends upon the existence of such biological individuality.

Now as soon as a society comes into being it acquires an individuality reminiscent of that of the primitive cell. This brings it promptly into competition with other similar entities of greater or less efficiency of organization. One of two courses may then follow. It may remain so loosely organized that its component members retain intact their own hard-won individualities and so merely pool their co-operative efforts without ever becoming wholly committed to the road of social specialization. Thus it evolves primarily through intracommunal selection among its members—a particularly dynamic and flexible course. On the other hand, if the society becomes firmly committed to unitary action, then in order to survive it must become as efficient an individual unit as possible, for now selection occurs *between* rather than *within* social groups. The members that make up its co-ordinate parts must then become highly specialized and their specialties must be tightly and efficiently integrated. In this process their own spheres of action and their own competence as individuals are inevitably narrowed.

This is the road that many—but not all—of the most conspicuous and striking societies in nature have taken.

There is a puzzling dilemma in this evolution. Its end point seems to be the formation of a society that will be as well integrated and efficiently co-ordinated and as much like an individual as possible. Yet at its very best no society can hope to achieve a better integration as an "individual" than can one of its own individual components. No colony of ants can become so well co-ordinated as is one of its own members. The community that is the Portuguese man-of-war has perhaps gone furthest in this direction. But even the great man-of-war is little more of an individual than is a solitary jellyfish. Thus if the development of an effective individuality is the goal of evolution, the question may well be put—why did expansion from the well-co-ordinated level of the individual to the poorly co-ordinated level of the primitive society ever take place?

The answer to this question is no simple one. The explanation, however, may lie once again in the forces of natural selection. For it can be argued that a well-integrated society, by virtue of its greater adaptability and plasticity and the greater competence and experience resulting from the close-knit specialized capacities of its members, may be more than a match for the solitary individual. But, while this may be true of the well-knit society at the end of the evolutionary road, it is hard to imagine that in the early struggling stages of its evolution any society was better fitted to survive than the solitary members from which it was formed. For example, is an adult community of *Stenogaster depressigaster* better off than the individuals of related species of solitary wasps which surround it in the Philippine Islands? It seems possible that its members are at some actual disadvantage because of the ties which restrict their activities.

Thus far the explanation is insufficient. However, it should be noted that the argument has proceeded upon an observation of primitive societies which consisted of groups of individuals permanently allied and partly dependent on each other and yet insufficiently co-ordinated to make up a smoothly functioning whole.

Balanced in a sense between a solitary and a social state, they have all the disadvantages of each. But there is an earlier stage in the evolution of these primitive societies.

This is the entity of the family—of solitary mud-dauber wasps, of robins, or of man. This prototype of the social way differs in a very important respect from the colony of Stenogastrine wasps or the community of bumblebees. Its juvenile members are dependent upon their parent or parents and perhaps upon one another during the period of their youth. But at maturity they become fully independent and the family then often dissolves. Such a situation as this may offer real advantages in natural selection to the species which adopts it. For the young individuals will have a better chance of survival during the transitory period of their helplessness, yet they will not need to become permanently attached to the group, for at maturity they will attain independence. The family type of organization may well have been adopted many times and among many species of living things—indeed, the simple family of this sort is perhaps the commonest of the presocial types in the world today. From this stage, other forces may have pushed some families on to the precarious stage so well represented by the Stenogastrine wasps. We shall later consider what these events may have been. Thenceforward survival in competition between groups might have required an evolutionary progress to the more spectacularly integrated forms of society.

In the evolution of societies these two trends to complexity and integration are like cross-currents. Social integration, a process which operates only at the level of life, is commonly preceded or accompanied by an expansion in complexity, which is the more universal trend. Among the solitary wasps, no consolidation of brood cells—the first integrative step toward the social mode—could take place until the habit of building brood cells, albeit widely scattered, had appeared. No worker caste could appear among the social bees until loose family associations had grown up among types once solitary. No political state was ever consolidated until fairly durable associations had developed among loosely co-ordinated groups within it. It is as if the first wasp colonies or the first colonial jelly-fish were brought to the crude beginnings of their social state by very special conditions not always directly related to straightforward natural selection.[1] Then, as they found themselves in a new and precarious situation, they went forward rapidly in evolution on the road to an integrated society.

This situation may in part account for the notable rarity of missing links in social evolution. The primitive social termite genera *Mastotermes* and *Archotermopsis* include only one known species each. Though both groups are known to have been wide-spread in Tertiary times, today they are respectively confined to a remote part of Australia and to the northwestern Himalayas—areas which may offer them protection from the main competitive stream of termite life. Yet their primitive relatives, the solitary cock-roaches, are vigorous and numerous the world over, and higher, thoroughly social termites abound in the tropics, and give every evidence of being dominant and well adjusted. Among the ants, which are insects as different from termites as could well be imagined, the most socially ancient and primitive forms, like the most socially ancient termites, are confined at present to remote

[1] These special situations in individual and social evolution are more fully considered later. One immediate and fascinating possibility may be this. Suppose that some of the progeny of these early families suffered "mutations" so that they were defective in certain ways. We know that such mutations do occur in many living things. If the organism were still solitary, such mutants, unable to care for themselves, would perish. If a family were already developed, however, they might receive protection, and compensate for their dependence by channeling their activities into promoting the family welfare. Such forms might not only survive, but might be an actual evolutionary advantage to the family, and such tendencies might actually be selected in the germ plasm of organisms just verging upon the social state. It is interesting to reflect that among solitary organisms, if defective individuals do not actually die in competition, they are often killed by normal members of their own species. But in the subsocial family, if one individual is defective, its brothers or sisters are quite likely to be defective also in similar ways. It is thus possible that such defectives might be mutually dependent, and would not suffer the hostility common to "loss mutants" among higher solitary creatures. This mutual dependence would tend greatly to strengthen the social ties of the family—as a family of crippled brothers or sisters might tend to dwell together throughout life.

and restricted areas like the Australian continent, save a few that have survived, as timid underground species, in protected situations elsewhere on the globe. Yet, as with the termites, the general solitary prototypes from which they arose persist in numbers today, while the socially highly developed forms that have followed them are common everywhere.

Again, among the jellyfish the socially intermediate genera of the Siphonophorans are less conspicuous than either the solitary jellyfish or the more perfectly adapted Portuguese man-of-war. It is as if the low point in the fortunes of a species occurred when it first awkwardly embarked on an integrated social life. If it does not rapidly develop from this position into a close-knit, well-coordinated community, it will be under such pressure from those better integrated solitary individuals which preceded it and the similarly better-integrated social units that are its successors that it will be doomed to a precarious existence in remote places, to ever-increasing diminution of its numbers, and perhaps to ultimate extinction.

Does this mean that a society's only road to survival is through increasing integration, through tighter and tighter organization and greater and greater subordination of the parts to the whole, until the units that compose it are reduced to the stature of helpless dependents? Such a conclusion, applied to the societies of men, becomes the totalitarian philosophy. The course which it outlines parallels the evolution of the totalitarian state as we have seen it in Nazi Germany, and as we see it with far greater force and elaboration today in Communist Russia. Whether this is the inevitable outcome of human evolution is the question for which we shall attempt to find an answer.

CHAPTER 4

Simplicity and Specialization

THE MARCH TO complexity of life and societies on earth can be halted or reversed in many ways. One of the more superficial may result from the unusual success of a single species of organism or a single kind of society in evolution in some particular part of the earth at some particular time. A single type may multiply to such an extent, and may so succeed in dominating its sphere, as to reduce sharply the total richness and variety of other flora and fauna. Thus the English sparrow or the starling may drive many native birds from the parks and woods about our cities and substitute a uniform population of its own kind. Thus also when the predatory and aggressive ant—*Pheidole megacephala*—landed in Madeira from the early sailing ships, it encountered a native ant fauna which must have been rather varied. Promptly and effectively it exterminated their societies, as it is now exterminating the native ant fauna of Bermuda.

Man, operating on the grandest territorial scale of all social predators, has sharply reduced the diversity of life forms over the whole earth. The weft of his social fabric has engulfed in their turn the great auk and the moa, the bison and the passenger pigeon, the heath hen and the Carolina parakeet. And following in the train of man has come another band of destroyers to reap where he has sown—rats and roaches, gulls and pheasants, dandelions and jimson weeds. All these add their bit to the further reduction in variety of the fauna and flora of the world.

47

Obviously, this aspect of the retreat from complexity primarily affects the diversity of forms in the living world. Although it may indirectly promote or retard an evolutionary trend to complexity within a society, it has little direct connection with that phenomenon. Moreover, despite the often apparently catastrophic effect of the ravages of a single species upon the variety of organisms over limited portions of the globe in a short-range view, it is doubtful whether such predation has ever been a permanently important factor in reversing or even in greatly stemming the tide of diversity in the long run. Dominant races of plants and animals have come and gone many times through the geologic ages. Each has tended, for a while, to populate vast spaces of the earth with uniform multitudes of its own kind at the expense of a host of more varied but less aggressive competitors. Passenger pigeons in their millions darkened the sky and so pre-empted whole woodlands that great branches broke under their weight. So likewise the bison hordes pre-empted the plains. So abundant were two species of coarse ferns in South America in the Mesozoic period that whole geological formations are characterized by their masses. They must have displaced a great variety of other flora. Yet in each case these abundant species had their day and died away, leaving the field free for the great tide of variation to repopulate it.

This, then, is probably not a very important kind of exception to the trend to complexity. But there are some others which seem to be much more fundamental. In these the trends to complexity and to integration of the structure of societies seem alike to have been halted or reversed in evolution. One of the most fascinating is the effect of abnormal conditions of moisture and temperature on the direction of social evolution.

We have seen that one explanation of the fact that the earth, and especially the life upon it, presents the grandest and most dynamic example of the trend to complexity known within the confines of the solar system is that the earth seems to be unique among the terrestrial planets in an important characteristic. Water is apparently a comparatively rare substance throughout much of the solar system. By contrast, it exists on earth in extraordinary abundance. Moreover, the terrestrial temperatures over most of the earth are such that water can exist in two, and often in three, of its natural states—as vapor, as liquid, and as ice. These two conditions, in conjunction, have had much to do with the spectacular tide to complexity so typical of earthly life.

Water has several characteristics which make it a substance of almost unique significance in biological reactions, and so of predominant importance in promoting evolution. Its polar character confers upon it broad and peculiar properties as a solvent and as a vehicle in which rapid interactions among dissolved substances may take place. It also enters into a large number of reactions which are concerned with life processes.

If the abundance of water and the equable temperature on earth are indeed deeply involved in the trend to complexity, then any disturbance of this peculiar and fortunate balance should arrest that trend on so cosmic a scale as to render insignificant the relatively minute and transient effects brought about through the passing dominance of any life-form. If this be so, the picture of life in those areas where the temperature-water balance is in fact upset should be of great interest. In these environments there ought to be a severe interruption, or even a reversal, of the trend to complexity.

The special places on earth where this optimum water-temperature balance is lost are manifest. Situations in which moisture is adequate but temperatures are extreme are to be found in the polar seas and in the permanent snowfields of the arctic regions or on the highest mountain summits. The other extreme of temperature, with water still abundant, is to be found naturally in such places as the thermal hot springs so characteristic of the volcanic areas of the earth, like those of Iceland, Yellowstone Park, and New Zealand. The converse situation—where temperatures are favorable but moisture is critical—obtains in the drier deserts of the world. More extreme examples are provided by the surfaces of bare rocks and the faces of newborn lava flows or by barren volcanic islands. The even more extreme situation of the brine lakes—such as the Great Salt Lake and the Dead Sea—are physiologically more arid for most life than all but the hottest and driest of deserts.

Consider first the state of the true society in the polar regions of the earth. It is patent that the societies of men in arctic regions are extremely simple. If the social development of the Eskimo, the Lapp, and the Patagonian was not arrested at an early stage and forced into more or less detailed specializations at a primitive level of organization, it must have returned to that condition from a more complex state. In either case, the trend to complexity has been markedly retarded.

Among invertebrates the same condition is even more vividly manifest at the level of the true society. Termites are known to occur only as far north as Quesnal Lake in British Columbia and in Ontario, and as far south as Patagonia. Their range does not extend nearly to the regions of permanent snow. It is, in fact, apparently limited by the mean annual isotherm of 50° Fahrenheit in both hemispheres. Yet even in the still comparatively warm areas at the geographic frontiers of their distribution, the species all belong to groups forming comparatively small, simple, and primitive communities. Those archaic termites—*Archotermopsis*—which penetrate to altitudes of nine thousand feet in the Himalayas and are therefore extraordinarily cold-resistant for such creatures, form probably the most primitive communities of these insects in the world. Along the whole northern and southern borders of the termite empire—in North and South America, in India and China, in Japan and Australia—the resident termite fauna exists in primitive or archaic societies. Only in the more tropical regions of the Americas, of Asia, Africa, and Australia, do highly socialized forms occur in their vastly populous and immensely complex city-states. Only in these areas too, is the termite fauna complex in the richness and variety of its species. In colder regions the number of species in any locality is successively reduced, until along the temperature boundaries of the range but few remain. At such places, as in the northeastern United States, vast areas may be occupied by only a single termite form.

The same trend toward a simplicity of colonial structure is to be observed at another point in the panorama of insect evolution as we compare the organization of insect societies in the warmer and cooler portions of their range. Only a very few wasps, for example, penetrate to regions that experience the intensities of arctic cold, and these species form some of the smallest and simplest of annual communities. Yet in the tropics related forms build societies that are large, complex, and perennial. Among the colonial bees, the bumblebees, which are notably primitive in their social habits, are predominantly inhabitants of the temperate zones of the world, although tropical forms are known which live in large, permanent associations. In the milder temperate regions, such as New Zealand and the northern Mediterranean areas, bumblebees are on the wing throughout the year and their communities attain considerable size and complexity, though they are probably not perennial and they do not approach the organizations of the tropical Melipone bees or those of the equally warmth-loving members of the honeybee group. But in such places as north central Europe and in the northern New England states, bumblebees, though abundant, are active for only three to six months of the year and form colonies for only a part of this period. Thus during much the greater portion of the annual cycle, the race is represented here only by the solitary young queens which survive through their first winter hidden away in cracks and crevices. Among these cold-weather types, communal existence is only an intermittent, evanescent stage in their life-cycle.

Still farther north, the hard-pressed bumblebee queen labors furiously through the long sunlit hours of the brief arctic summer to establish a colony and rear a few workers before the new generation of perfect females and males must appear and the social phase be terminated. Shorter and shorter grows the time available for the development of this social phase as the pioneer arctic species of *Bombus* push toward the permanent snows. Simpler and simpler are the communities which they are able to maintain. It has been assumed, although it is not certainly known, that at last, in the snow-loving types, such as *Bombus hyperboreus* and *Bombus kirbyellus*, it is impossible for the queen ever to rear many workers or to establish a community in the true sense. The parent may finally be permanently reduced to the status of a solitary bee, tending her single brood of perfect daughters and sons, which disperses soon after it has attained maturity.

The ants are in similar case. Their communities, to be sure, are permanent wherever they occur. A few species range far into the cold places of the earth, eking out a poverty-stricken existence among the melting snow pools of high mountain meadows or in the spongy arctic tundra well beyond the tree line. But the simple colonies of such hardy pioneers are vastly different in size and in complexity from the city-states of the tropical fungus growers or the vast restless armies of the African and South American driver ants.

As with the bumblebees, the role of caste is much reduced among the arctic ants. Indeed, there is barely time in the short summer for colonies of certain species of *Formica* to produce a generation of workers before the young queens and males must be born and growing. The two events may occur simultaneously. Queens are abnormally abundant in the nests of many such ants, sometimes almost replacing the population of worker personnel in their numbers and threatening to reduce the colonial structure once again to the simple one of males and perfect females. The workers commonly exhibit a monotony of form and physique, strikingly different from the bizarre variety of caste so characteristic of many tropical species.

This relative lack of social differentiation suggests that of forms that are actually primitive. Yet, in sharp contrast to the primitive types, such species are actually far advanced in evolution and are most nearly related to temperate or tropical types that show a much greater complexity of social organization. Clearly the trend to complexity has at the very least been retarded, if it has not actually been reversed.

Consider now the converse set of circumstances, in which temperature is within the range for dynamic organic and social evolution, but the supply of water is critically low. The most evident environment of this type is that of the almost waterless deserts. Here, at the social level of man, there can be detected an evolutionary shift under certain circumstances from more complex to more simple forms of social organization. Thus recent ethnological evidence indicates that the exquisitely adapted social structure of such peoples as the Hopi, simple, uniform, and monotonous as it is, stemmed in ages past from a social complex perhaps resembling that of the Indians of the Mexican and Isthmian region, of which the great state of the Aztecs was a spectacular offshoot. The wandering peoples of the Arabian desert maintain to this day a nomad culture exquisitely fitted to its environment but on the whole simple in structure and function; yet no ethnologist would deny the potentialities for complex organization inherent in the Arab peoples—potentialities which are fully realized in the cities or in periods of great social tension such as war. It is probable that there have never been organizations of humans existing in any of the drier deserts which are as highly complex as our urbanized civilizations.

The same situation appears to obtain among the social insects. Small as they are, often resistant to desiccation, and amazingly keen in finding their water requirements, the social insects are able to maintain themselves in abundance in areas too dry to support any complex human social structure. However, the number and variety of their species is considerably reduced. Some of the most highly evolved social groups of termites flourish in many parts of the Australian and African deserts, and social bees, wasps, and ants all occupy such areas in great numbers. But in the truly dry environments, where the water lack is serious even for such small organisms, they cease to be abundant. There are few social insects, save a handful of species of highly modified ants, which are able to persist continuously in the hearts of dry and shifting sand dunes. Bees and wasps dwell here, to be sure, but they obtain their water from a distance. The earthbound social insects are conspicuous for their rarity. Among the sands of the seashore, where the water, being salt, is as unavailable to most social insects as it would be to man, such insects are similarly rare, save for a few hardy invaders and temporary occupants. On the bare sheets of hardened and unweathered lava flows and on the surfaces of new-risen volcanic islands there are virtually no types of social insects in permanent residence.

There are indications of similar trends among multicellular animals and plants. On the sun-scorched and virtually waterless surfaces of bare rocks, the first conspicuous multicellular plants that manage to become established are characteristically certain lichens—the crustose forms. These greedily drink the water which falls as rain or dew and tenaciously retain the niggard moisture. Through the merciless days of sunshine which follow they dry out slowly and reluctantly. Such lichens are actually elementary botanical communities composed of two kinds of cells, each belonging to a simple and lowly plant group. The color of the structure is furnished by primitive terrestrial algae. These, able as they are to manufacture carbohydrates photosynthetically, furnish most of the food for the association. In return, they receive protection from drying out by the water-holding, sun-resisting web of colorless fungus in which they are embedded.

No plant can long occupy such a well-nigh waterless environment as a bare rock-face without changing the character of that environment to some extent. Bit by bit the lichens extend their clinging tentacles beneath the superficial layers of the stone. Bit by bit the surface yields and scales off in small patches. Ultimately the lichens may have penetrated for a distance of several millimeters. Bit by bit the debris of this process of penetration, composed of earthlike rock dust, piles up about the lichen patch, adding its mite to the waterholding capacity of the system and contributing a little to its protection from the full glare of the sunshine.

On quartzite or basaltic stones in dry climates the reduction of the rock face may be so slow, and the accumulation of moisture so slight, that such simple conditions as these may persist for a hundred years. On soft sandstone or limestone in a moist region, this stage in the evolution of complexity within the tiny system may be very much shorter. In any event, ultimately there comes a time when enough organic debris has accumulated about the lichens so that the extreme condition of moisture lack has eased a little and the most rigorous period has passed. With this change comes an increase in the complexity of the life system, both from the standpoint of the variety of its flora and from that of the level of cellular organization of the plants occupying it.

Newcomers appear on the rock. Quite usually they are leafy lichens, larger than the crustlike varieties, and attached to the underlying layers at a single point or along a single margin. These lichens raise conspicuous upstanding crinkled blades, reminiscent in superficial appearance of those of some marine algae. These broad, leaflike branches expand rapidly over the pioneer forms, absorbing light and competing mercilessly for moisture. As they increase in size they invade more aggressively, until at last the earlier occupants relinquish the ground which had been so hardly won. In slowly dying off and decaying, they add another mite to the soil that is in the building.

Scarcely has this change occurred when still another class of invaders appears. These are the dry-land mosses, often spearheaded in their attack by the black and hair mosses or by tortuously twisted forms. For long these most recent arrivals may contest the rock with the leafy lichens, and the two may persist side by side. But the mosses consistently grow on above as they die out below, forming a dense, continuous mat in which a relatively thick layer of humus accumulates, in sharp contrast to the thin film of soil characteristically laid down by the leafy lichens. This constant overgrowth by the more complex and massive mosses ultimately overwhelms their lichen competitors and they are left in temporary command of the situation.

Their ascendancy, however, is short-lived. For now at last a thin but true soil substrate has been laid down and stabilized. It forms the basis for a miniature garden. The seeds of higher annual plants quickly find a lodging. They germinate, grow, and fruit with great rapidity. Now the system has become complex indeed. The annuals contribute markedly to the accumulation of humus and go far to increase the water-retaining properties of the system. From here on, the environment can no longer be regarded as a desiccated one. It progresses more or less rapidly through its subsequent stages of complexity. It is successively colonized by biennial and perennial herbs and then by shrubs of increasing size. Finally, as the rocks disintegrate or become buried in the gathering humus, the association reaches its culmination in the climax forest, with all its wealth of flora and fauna.

In this way it is possible to trace in miniature an actual increase of complexity in organic life with the increase of moisture, while the temperature factor remains unchanged. The process can readily be experimentally reversed. As the moisture content decreases, so will the succession of living forms and their variety in the environment gradually decrease in complexity until at last the crustlike lichens are the sole survivors among multicellular organisms. If water is withheld to the point where even the lichens cannot survive, the multicellular level of evolution is eliminated altogether. Then there are left only bacteria and fungus spores, and possibly the dormant forms of a few unicellular algae. As in extreme temperatures, life under conditions of extreme drought will make its last stand at the least complex level of existence—that of the single cell. This is the end. If the rock is maintained in a waterless state for a sufficient length of time, in the end it will probably become wholly sterile, though the years required for this final step of extinction may be far more than the life span of any man.

This retrogression from complexity to the severe simplicity of life under conditions of extreme dryness may occur under certain conditions with startling rapidity. At the level of the unicellular bacteria and algae and fungi the whole evolution, except the very last stage in which life becomes extinct, can be accomplished within a few days within the confines of a single culture dish. And, once the transition has occurred, the condition of complexity can be restored as quickly by moistening the dried medium.

One more natural environment is of interest in connection with the effects of drought. This is the situation in the brine lakes of the world, in the temporary salt pans of the deserts, and in the larger, more permanent bodies of salt-saturated water, such as Great Salt Lake and the Dead Sea. When there are concentrations of salt in the soil above about 1 per cent in terms of dry soil weight, or its equivalent in water, moisture will actually be lost from the tissues of most plants and animals dwelling there. Only those organisms with an exceptional composition of protoplasm and exceptional qualities of cell-wall permeability can resist extreme desiccation under these conditions.

Accordingly, the fauna of the extremely salty lakes is a very meager one. It includes no examples of true societies. In the Great Salt Lake of Utah, for example, only two multicellular animals apparently occur—the larva of a fly and a primitive little brine shrimp—both highly specialized to their strange environment. It is equally hard to find examples among the many-celled plants. A beautiful gradation to simplicity of plant structure with increasing saline concentration is to be seen about the margins of the brine lakes in our own West. At terrestrial concentrations of salt of between 1 and 2 per cent of the dry weight of the soil in which they grow, such higher plants as the sea blite and the saltwort will flourish, and a salt grass may persist at the upper range of salinity.

Beyond this point plants with a system adapted for conducting water are in general unable to survive, and the field is left to certain specialized algae, which may exist in concentrations of salt as high as 25 per cent. At this highest end of the concentration scale, however, even the simplest representatives of multicellular existence eventually disappear, and the field is left to unicellular forms. In Searles Lake, California, where the water contains more than 30 per cent of dissolved solids and the excess salt may actually form a crust over the water strong enough to bear the weight of several men, the salt sheet is colored a bright green by species of such algae. By virtue of special adjustments of protoplasmic constitution they are able to extract water even from so unpromisingly arid an environment. These salt-living algae, like those of the snows or of the hot springs, form a restricted and specialized group, and they occur only in the peculiar and extreme habitats to which they are suited. Yet their geographic distribution is global and there is scarcely a salt pan that is not tenanted by some of them.

Thus there is a striking similarity in the flora and the fauna of these environments of extreme cold and heat and desiccation, which sets them sharply apart from the denizens of the rest of the world. In general they have not been recruited from directly related groups of plants or animals. The simplicity and specialization of such populations, in terms of rarity and paucity of variety of forms and general lowliness of organization at both the multicellular and the social level of existence, must therefore be thought of as a parallel development. It seems indicative indeed of the role which the temperature and the abundance of water on the planet have played in accelerating and expanding the trend to complexity. It illustrates the profound influence that a series of non-living, non-biological parameters may have on the course of evolution to complexity of organisms and the societies that they build.

CHAPTER 5

The Parasite on the Host and the Individual in the Society

JUST AS LIFE, through its creation of complex environments, can accelerate the trend to complexity in evolution, so also it is often a most potent factor in reversing that trend. This reversal can be spectacular when the environments that life provides are uniform or specialized. Nowhere is this strange situation more pointedly evident than in the institution of parasitism.

Parasitism is by no means easy to define. One reason for this is that, as commonly considered, it comprehends so many types of association between living things. Thus in compound plants like lichens, a fungus and an alga can become permanently welded in a mutually beneficial alliance. In other cases the association may be largely neutral. The various harmless bacteria which inhabit a man's skin are an example of this. Again, the benefit of the partnership may be very one-sided, but still may result in no particular harm for the exploited party. This is the case with the marine sucker-fish *Remora,* one or more of which attach themselves to a shark by the specialized suction caps on the top of their heads and ride about without effort, ready at any moment to drop away when the shark has made a kill so that they may feed in company with their involuntary host. Finally, the partner which benefits by the relationship may, in procuring that benefit, injure its host—as in the case of a noxious bacterial disease afflicting a plant, an animal, or a man.

Parasitism may be of many kinds in yet another sense. Whole societies can subsist as parasites on other societies. Again, solitary organisms can be parasitic on societies. Or finally, neglecting the numerous situations in which single cells are parasites, there are the interesting and varied cases in which solitary many-celled organisms are parasitic on similar solitary hosts.

About three thousand species of solitary insects, of the widest range of types and forms, seek their lodging or maintain a living within the nests of ants. Among the most elementary of these relationships is that of the little springtails, technically known as Podurans. Certain of these tiny active sprites live as indifferently tolerated ant-guests, flitting about the nest apparently undetected by their hosts and picking up debris or stray bits of food like the street pigeons of our cities. These guests are harmless enough to their social benefactors and are but little modified to live among them, save as they are apparently gifted with a neutral odor and with sprightly ways whereby they slip unobserved through the densest throng. Similar in kind, though of much greater menace to the ants, are certain flesh-eating beetles. These lurk about the fringes of the colony, hiding in deserted galleries and feeding like jackals upon refuse and the bodies of dead ants, or preying from ambush upon unwary living workers remote from help. Such predators as these are well recognized as enemies by the ants; but like stealthy wolves about a primitive human community, they are rarely captured.

The ants extend little hospitality either to the harmless springtails or to the dangerous beetles. For both of these existence in the nest and access to the scraps from the social table are precarious and can be maintained only at the cost of perpetual watchfulness. There is nothing particularly striking in such a relationship, which is essentially that of the pariah dog in the Indian village. It is when the intruder develops characteristics which render it pleasing to the ants, and so earns tolerance or even eager acceptance in the heart of the community, that the situation becomes much more interesting.

A simple example of acceptance (in this case occurring outside the community) is provided by a curious Japanese bug—*Ptilocerus*. Taking up a station near the foraging columns of some ant species, it draws itself erect and displays a series of brilliant red tufts of hair. These are supplied with a fluid the odor of which is evidently highly attractive to the potential victims. The combination of the odor and the tufts is too much. Before long the bug is surrounded by ants, avidly licking and tugging. For some time it submits quietly. But, as has been experimentally demonstrated, the secretion on the hairs has a narcotic effect on the imbibers. Soon they become quiet; ultimately they collapse in death. Thereupon the bug inserts its sharp beak into each of the corpses and drains it dry. A nicely specialized bit of predation, this. But it can hardly be considered parasitism, since the bug never inhabits the nests of the ants, and is never protected by them.

A more highly evolved example of nest parasitism is furnished by a peculiar butterfly, the extraordinary life history of which has been fully elucidated only in recent years. The British Large Blue —*Maculinea arion,* a member of the Lycaenidae—is a beautiful Lepidopteran of a brilliant cerulean hue. Having a wingspread of perhaps an inch, it is a veritable giant of its pygmy tribe. It is confined largely to the south of England, ranging into Cornwall and along the Cotswolds. There it deposits its eggs in June on the buds of the wild thyme. These shortly hatch into normal-appearing caterpillars which proceed to nibble on the vegetation about them. For about twenty days they feed and grow uneventfully, passing through three molts. During this time, they show little deviation from the standard pattern of most butterfly larvae, except that they are carnivorous as well as leaf feeders. At the third molt, however, a most significant change takes place.

The larva ceases to feed, deserts the thyme on which it has grown, and travels about aimlessly. At the same time, a "honey gland" begins to function actively. After a bit of wandering, the larva meets with some foraging ants of a particular species common in the locality. At once it is given the greatest attention. For some time it submits to being licked and fondled. Finally its thorax begins to swell and ultimately the forward segments become enormously distended. At this stage an ant picks it up and carries it off to the nest. Here the caterpillar is deposited among the ant brood, and here it remains—from midsummer until the following June. During the first summer it feeds avidly upon the ant grubs which lie about it, grows enormously, and changes radically in appearance. At the end of six weeks it comes to look more like an ant larva than caterpillar. It has become fat, white, and helpless, rather resembling a sausage.

Over the winter it hibernates, and in the spring it begins again to feed on ant young. This gorging continues until it is ready to pupate. With great difficulty it then crawls up onto the roof of the chamber where it has long lain helpless but well cared for and spins a pad of silk. Hanging from this precarious support, it transforms into a chrysalis. Shortly, however, the white chrysalid falls from its perch back among the ant young, and here it remains until the perfect butterfly finally emerges with tiny, unexpanded wings. This immature adult creeps away from the brood chamber where it has developed, gradually making its way up and out of the nest into the sunlight. Here the handsome iridescent blue pinions expand. At long last the butterfly flits away to enter upon its mature life in perfectly conventional fashion, to deposit its eggs on the wild thyme blossoms, and ultimately to perish.

A point of particular interest about this case of the parasitism of an individual on a society is that it appears to represent an intermediate stage of development—a halfway point, as it were, in the evolution of this form of social parasitism. The Large Blue adult is a completely independent individual. Neither its structure nor its habits suggest that it differs in any significant way from dozens of other species of Blues that are common the world over. Moreover, in its early stages, there is little about the caterpillar to suggest that it will take up a parasitic mode of life. While its honey gland is attractive to ants, this is a common condition among the European Blues, as well as among many of their near butterfly relatives, most of which are known to be non-parasitic.

Only when the caterpillar has become established among the ant brood in a parasitic relationship do physical modifications ensue involving simplification and specialization of structure and behavior to its sedentary mode of life. Correspondingly, it is only the older larva and the pupa of the Large Blue which differ strikingly from the similar stages of other related but independent forms. The trend to specialization and simplification has not invaded any other phase of the life cycle. Not even the egg-laying instincts of the adult are modified. This corresponds with the fact that the initiation and conduct of the parasitic phase of the life cycle rests primarily with the half-grown larva.

This curious segregation of the parasitic habit to a phase of immature life, with a restriction of simplification of structure and habit also confined to that phase, can be even more vividly illustrated. There is a solitary wasplike creature—*Schizaspidia tenuicornis*—in northern Japan which presents an extraordinary contrast between the complexity of structure and instinct displayed by its larvae upon hatching and the extreme simplification which they undergo once they have attained an appropriate location for parasitism. In its adult phase this creature is winged and free-living, sometimes soaring to considerable heights. The fertile females, emerging in late summer, are strongly attracted to the newly formed winter buds of mulberry and chestnut trees. There, often well up in the treetops, each individual quickly deposits *en masse* between the bud scales a thousand or so minute eggs. These buds become so packed that they are greatly distended with ova. Eggs may actually squeeze out between the scales.

Within the buds the eggs pass the winter in a dormant condition. The following spring the majority of the buds expand and the scales drop to the ground. The attached eggs, it must be presumed, hatch, but the young soon perish. Thus a large share of each brood is probably lost at the very beginning of life. However, a small proportion of the buds die during the winter and the scales stick to the twigs, becoming somewhat separated as they dry. When the eggs that have adhered to these few dead buds hatch, the larvae have a possible chance of survival, but it is still far from good.

From such an egg there emerges an athletic little larva dark in color and heavily armored. This specialized creature—called a "planidium"—has numerous sensory hairs along its body surface and is equipped with a powerful sucking disk. With the aid of these devices, and by dint of well-developed body muscles and a rather highly organized nervous system, it is able to move about freely and to jump considerable distances. It requires no food and is equipped to undergo prolonged fasting. Indeed, it stands in dire need of these characteristics. For its parent—far from adequately providing for its future as a parasite—has placed it in about as remote and difficult a position as could be found. Its only hope of reaching an ant's nest is to be carried there as a passive rider. Upon this tenuous possibility is staked its entire chance of further development.

Crawling from the bud in which it has hatched to a likely position on a twig or leaf, the young planidium takes up its station. Propped bolt upright and firmly attached by its sucker, it begins an often unrewarded vigil. It can maintain this immobile and watchful wait for about three weeks. After this it will perish from lack of sustenance. If fortune favors, a foraging ant of the proper species passes by within an inch or so before the planidium is exhausted and possibly pauses near by to milk a plantation of aphids. In that instant the wary planidium jumps aboard. When the ant thus afflicted finally returns to its nest the parasite makes a further transfer—this time to the brood pile of the ants. Here, after some maneuvering, it selects a mature ant larva to be its future host. Then it suddenly undergoes a molt, emerging as a lightly armored shining white grub which is virtually devoid of organs of either sense or locomotion. It is as unlike its earlier self as can well be imagined.

It is now a true parasite. The simplification of structure and function which accompanied this change of existence has occurred with almost explosive suddenness. It has just enough motive power left to attach itself to the host of its choice in a characteristic position. The ant larva shortly spins a cocoon over both the parasite and itself and inside this transforms to a pupa. Thereupon the parasite makes a single feeding hole in its host and, rapidly draining its contents, kills it. At the same time the parasite now grows enormously, becoming almost incapable of any ordered movement. Within a week it matures and pupates. Six days later the adult cuts its way out of the ant cocoon and follows the tortuous galleries of the nest to the surface of the soil, where it emerges into the sunshine.

If it is a female, it is met at the nest entrance by a cloud of hovering males and is fertilized. Immediately afterward it ascends into the treetops to deposit its eggs—this in utter disregard of the fact that if the parent merely paused at the entrance of the ants' nest to drop its eggs there in the dust the larvae hatching from them would have a considerably better chance of survival. Within the day the *Schizaspidia* female usually dies, having taken no food.

Thus the insect which has spent almost twelve months within the egg, much of this time as a mature larva patiently awaiting the propitious moment to break out—which may wait an additional three weeks as a tiny planidium in motionless vigil for the opportunity to secure passage to the only situation in which it can grow further—requires but two weeks to complete all the rest of its development and persists only a day or two at the climax of its life. Truly this is an intense specialization to permit a bare survival amid the extreme hazards that may surround the existence of a parasite!

No simplified or degenerate features can be seen in either structure or instincts in the adult phase of the Large Blue, unless it is the delayed expansion of the wings which facilitates its exit from its underground prison. Likewise there are no particular modifications in the larva before the third molt, though after this period they appear in profusion. But with the Japanese *Schizaspidia* the situation is somewhat different. Here both egg and planidium are markedly specialized—the former in its long period of incubation, the latter in its high sensory endowment and resistant constitution. The adult, too, is greatly specialized in the habit of depositing its eggs all at once with machine-gun rapidity, in its lack of all organs for feeding, and in its very short life. But the significant fact is that the extreme simplification of structure and instinct typically accompanying a parasitic existence is sharply restricted to the actual portion of the life cycle spent within the ants' nest. The contrast between the active planidium and the degenerate larva after it has undergone its first molt in the nest is much more striking than that between the second- and third-stage caterpillars of the Large Blue.

Elsewhere among the relatives of this parasitic wasp there occur modifications of the maternal instinct in the adult adapted to the dependent mode of life of the larva which are lacking in *Schizaspidia*. Under such conditions the larva has no need to go through an initial phase of independence. Here the parasitic stage includes the whole juvenile period, and the larva begins life as a much simplified and even degenerate animal. These adaptations of the maternal instinct sometimes reach an extraordinary degree of precision, and the most exquisite discernment is displayed by the mother in placing her eggs in precisely the situations best suited for their subsequent development. In one type—the hymenopterous parasite *Coccophagus scutellaris*—the larvae are typically internal parasites of other insects, but the male and female young exhibit a surprising difference in their developmental requirements. The immature female is an internal parasite of a species of scale insect, burrowing into its tissues and ultimately devouring it. The young male, however, is internally parasitic upon the *parasite* of a scale insect, and usually upon a female larva of its own species!

The adult female must therefore make nice distinctions when laying her eggs. If the ova which she deposits are destined to produce females, she must select healthy scale insects of the proper species and insert the ova directly within the bodies of the hosts. However, she must behave quite differently if her eggs are to produce males. Then she must seek out those scale insects already parasitized by female grubs of her own species which are nearly mature. Puncturing these larvae, she must place her clutch of eggs within their tissues. Thus for every male larva which matures a young female must be sacrificed. Thus the only adult females available to carry on the species are those which have been overlooked as larvae by the adult females of the preceding generation.

However, it is also true that females are male-producing only until they have met an adult male and become fertilized. They therefore seek out female larvae to parasitize only until that time. Thereafter they concentrate their attention upon healthy unparasitized scales, and the eggs which they lay will produce female larvae, some of which will later serve as hosts for the male progeny of other adult females as yet unfertilized. The consequence is that each adult male, although it has destroyed a female larva in the course of its growth, actually increases the number of maturing females in the following generation manyfold provided only that it can find an infertile female and mate. For on the one hand, by the act of fertilization it transforms the whole gamut of instincts of its mate so that the latter will no longer prey on female larvae of its own species. On the other hand, it ensures that all eggs thereafter produced from that union will give rise to new females. The calculation of the optimum sex ratio would present a nice problem in biological statistics when applied to this extraordinary species which is in part a parasite upon itself!

There is another startling example of this extraordinary evolution of the maternal instinct. There are many insect parasites, mostly of rather minute stature, which complete their metamorphosis within the eggs rather than the larvae of larger insects. Now,

under the best of conditions insect eggs provide a limited environment in which to develop. The problem of crowding frequently
becomes acute. The less specialized of these parasites are careless
about this housing problem. A single female may deposit so many
eggs upon its host that the resulting young early come into fierce
competition and only one or a very few can survive. The more advanced hymenopteran parasites, however, are usually much more
accurate in their appraisal of the capacity of the host tissues. A
striking case in point is that of *Telenomus*.

This genus includes a group of small parasites which infest the
ova of butterflies and some other insects. The young female, having
found an egg of the proper host species, first examines it most carefully. If there is any evidence that another female has preceded
her she leaves, continuing her search for unmolested eggs. When
one is finally found, she pierces its shell and lays her own single
egg within it. She then proceeds to scrape a number of circular
lines about the puncture with her egg-laying organ. Improbable
as it may seem, the evidence is good that these lines actually function as a brand marking the egg as pre-empted and not subject to
further attack. For when another female arrives and finds these
blemishes she passes this egg by.

In these situations, the adaptation of the behavior of the adult
to the parasitic life of the larva has been developed to a high degree, primarily in the psychic rather than in the structural sphere.
There is certainly no simplification of structure in the adult phase
—rather, the reverse is true. But in larval life simplification and
degeneracy are evident from the very outset. This is consistent with
the fact that the entire existence of the larva is spent inactively in
sheltered and well-provided circumstances. It is as though the
trend to simplicity—which can occur only in that portion of the life
cycle which is truly parasitic—had advanced from its restricted
scope in the late larval period of the Large Blue to cover a very
large part of larval life in the Japanese *Schizaspidia*, and finally to
include the whole of larval existence in those parasites in which
the adults are so endowed as to make this extension possible.

It is not essential that the parasitic period, with its consequent simplification of endowment, shall come within the larval, as distinct from the adult, portion of the life cycle. It can just as well supervene at maturity, if that is when the sheltered portion of the life cycle occurs. Certain angler-fishes, for example, present a sequence in many respects almost the reverse of those thus far considered. These are strange fish of the middle ocean depths, where the females, blackish in color and huge of gape, range in perpetual darkness for their prey. The male of one angler-fish—*Photocorynus* —when first hatched shows quite as high a degree of structural organization as does the female. But it is inherently a parasite, and the function of this active phase is to seek out a suitable host. That host is a female of the same species. These familiar general features, however, mark the end of any similarity with the preceding cases. For the parasitism is not detrimental to the host, but on the contrary is distinctly functional for the species. The effect on the parasite, however, is virtually the same.

Having found a suitable female, the tiny young male bites a hole in the skin of the larger fish and inserts its movable "tongue." A fleshy projection is shortly formed around the wound, and the lips of the male may eventually fuse with it. Gradually the boundaries between the bodies of the two fish are largely broken down. Sheets of tissue grow up to unite the pair in a true Siamese-twin relationship. Ultimately the mouth of the male becomes almost completely blocked.

The male is now a permanent parasite. There will be no alteration of this situation throughout its life, no sudden assumption of an independent mode of existence at maturity like that which characterizes the insect parasites considered. The degeneracy and simplification of structure become emphasized with time, and at full maturity the male is little more than a tiny sac attached to the female. Its body becomes almost devoid of internal organs save a huge reproductive apparatus whereby copious sperm is secreted to fertilize the eggs of its mate as they are produced.

Thus the dependent mode of existence may be assumed at any

stage of a parasite's life cycle and the simplifications incident to it will normally be obvious only during that stage. It would be very surprising, however, if in the evolution of parasite-host relations the period of dependency did not in some cases come to cover the whole life span of the parasite. Thus its entire development would occur on or within the tissues of its host, and the whole phase of independent existence would disappear. This evolution seems to have occurred many times and in many places. It is extremely interesting to inquire whether the parasite shows, in such cases, simplification and degeneracy of structure throughout all the phases of its life cycle.

A stage of this development, transitional to the final one of permanent parasitism, is to be seen quite clearly among a number of insects in which the larvae are already internal parasites but in which the mature female, too, is becoming parasitic, often upon the adults of the same insect which in its immature stages serves as host for her young. Such a creature—the hymenopterous parasite *Rielia*—typically oviposits in the eggs of the praying mantis. The adult females are alert to place their eggs in the proper situations for immediate development. The device used to ensure this is a curious one. The female parasites seek out adult mantis females which have not yet laid, and attach themselves firmly. Here they ride about, perhaps for months, apparently sustaining themselves by feeding on secretions from the mantid's body until it is ready to oviposit. When this is done the parasite quickly deposits her own ova within the mantid egg mass before its frothy covering can harden into an impenetrable armor.

The larvae which hatch are internal parasites like those already considered, and are simplified in bodily structure accordingly. But the adult female, once it has attached itself to its mantid, also becomes a parasite, although it is an external one and its relationship to its host is not nearly so intimate as that of the larva. Crude as this adult parasitism is, however, it is reflected in the structure of the adult. For soon after she arrives and attaches herself, the parasite sheds her wings and undergoes various other simplifications of structure.

All these parallels of development among parasites suggest strongly that there are features of their protected existences which are universal and far-reaching in their effects. Just as winglike surfaces exist in all those larger organisms adapted to spending time in the air—be they birds, bats, flying squirrels, pterodactyls, volplaning lizards, or flying fish or insects—so all parasites that have achieved any degree of intimacy with their hosts exhibit a marked specialization. Are there selectional factors at work here of such effectiveness as to negate the more general movement to complexity, or is some other underlying cause or series of causes responsible for this convergence? The attempts to answer this question constitute one of the most fascinating fields of modern biology, and the problem is very far indeed from solution today. In another chapter an attempt is made to explore some of the trends of thinking through which such an answer may some day be derived.

The Individual in the Society

There is another aspect of this trend to simplicity in parasitism, of even greater fascination and importance, which is directly relevant to the problem of societies. This is the extent to which the member of a society is in reality a parasite upon its own organization. Society is the creation of the individual. When the individual is viewed in the setting of its society, however, it presents many aspects which suggest the parasite. Like the parasite, the social individual lives a sheltered and relatively uniform life. In many aspects of its existence it is shielded from the imperative demands that constantly confront a solitary organism. Concomitantly, in many instances the individual—again like the parasite—has undergone simplifications of structure and function in the course of its evolution. Moreover, just as the parasite shows greater specialization the longer its association with its host, so the individual often shows a progressive loss of over-all capabilities the more highly evolved is its society.

Abundant examples of this situation are to be found in the communities of men, though the evidence, while definite, is often relatively tenuous, as it is in so many other aspects of human socialization. There is little doubt for instance, that the young infants of highly civilized peoples are less well developed and more helpless than are the infants of humans at a lower stage of social evolution. Moreover, both are physically inferior to the infant primate of comparable age.

The same trend toward a suppression of development in the individual is to be seen with greater clarity among the members of well-knit social groups below the level of human society. Among ants the most intensely socialized species have young which are the least endowed physically, while the larvae of the primitive ants are active and athletic. The latter, poorly cared for as they are, must make their own way to the food scraps scattered about the nest by their comparatively indifferent nurses, must feed without assistance, and must ward off fierce attacks from hungry brood mates. On the other hand, the young of the highly social species are assiduously cared for by attentive nurses, are fed largely on liquid food administered directly by mouth or on minutely pulverized solid food placed within easy reach, and are carried about and scrupulously grouped and regrouped in sensitive response to changes of temperature and moisture within the nest. They are small-jawed and weak, lying like so many helpless white mummies on the floors of their brood chambers. Among many of them the capacity to spin cocoons has disappeared, so that they perforce transform to naked pupae.

The same trend shows itself in the adult phases of many social insects. Among ants this simplification of structure involves the reduction in the worker of several parts of the thorax, consistent with the loss of the wing muscles, the partial atrophy of the reproductive apparatus, often the loss of portions of the sensory equipment, and various other specializations. Among the termites the situation is particularly interesting. Here the final mature form of the adult workers of the highly socially evolved species frequently corresponds quite closely in structure to that of immature nymphs in other, more primitive types. The permanent workers of the higher genera may thus actually represent arrested infantile forms of the lower ones. Again, queen honeybees, because of the habit of swarming, do not go through the phase of independent colony formation characteristic of so many of the social insects. In a real sense they are permanent parasites on their own colonies. They are simpler in certain aspects of structure and instinct endowment than their corresponding worker forms.

These bits of evidence strongly suggest that the individuals in a society may be subject to a trend of simplification and specialization convergent to that of a parasite upon such a society. So far, the evolution of the individual toward the normal state of a parasite has been considered. Conversely, a social parasite, under the proper conditions, can evolve toward a state of perfect adjustment to its host, ultimately acquiring essentially the status of an individual in that society.

Among the thousands of insects which have taken up their abode in ants' nests is a group of short-winged staphylinid beetles. Predacious and aggressive, they are long and slender, flexible in body and alert in advancing their own cause. The least socially adapted of this group of insects can hardly be considered a true ant guest at all. Rather it is to be classed among those jackal-like predators which lurk on the fringes of the colony to pull down isolated individuals. Such predators are driven off by the ants whenever possible, but they are rarely actually captured or killed, and they quickly return as soon as opportunity offers. In one group of staphylinids, however—the Lomechusini—the parasitic relation has progressed much further.

Lomechusa is a flexible-bodied beetle with a reddish covering looking as though it had been freshly oiled, and decorated along the sides of the abdomen with tufts of long golden hairs. These are evidently covered with some substance highly attractive to ants. In consequence, far from being expelled like their more primitive associates, they are warmly welcomed in the colonies—of *Formica sanguinea*—where they dwell and are cleaned and fed regularly by the ants. However, they are still basically predatory in habit. Whenever possible they eke out the fare given them with a meat diet consisting of the bodies of ants or ant young.

The beetles lay their eggs within the nest without any attempt at protection. These ova are promptly picked up by the ants and placed with their own young, where they get equal care. When they are hatched, the rather helpless larvae lie among the ant brood, and are regularly cared for and fed by the ant nurses, often so enthusiastically that the ant brood suffers through neglect. It suffers in other ways too, for the larva, like the adult, is highly carnivorous and supplements the diet provided by its nurses with frequent meals upon the helpless ant young lying about it.

With all this attention and rich food supply, it is not surprising that the alien beetle population of the colony increases rapidly once this pest is established. The only hazard to its protected existence comes from a curious bit of mishandling on the part of the ants. In order to pupate, the mature beetle larva needs to be buried in the soil. This is a situation familiar to the ants, for their own larvae also require to be covered with earth before they can spin their cocoons. But the ants exhume their own cocoon-spinning young as soon as the silken coverings have had time to harden. Now, there is nothing in the instinct endowment of the ants to prompt them to differentiate between the requirements of their own and the beetle young. Accordingly, the ants exhume all the parasite larvae they can find a few hours after these have been buried and clean them as carefully as they do their own. This is fatal to the young beetles, which perish rather quickly. Fortunately for the beetle population, however, the ants are not skillful in finding all their buried charges, and enough escape detection to allow the parasite to increase rapidly.

As time goes on, more and more beetle adults and young accumulate. More and more of the time and energy of the ant workers is consumed in caring for them. The developing ant brood comes to suffer privation, attacked and decimated on the one hand by the parasite larvae and starved and neglected on the other by their own nurses. Eventually a curiously deformed caste of adults, known as *pseudogynes,* begins to appear in the nests and rapidly increases in numbers. In many respects these are intermediate between queen and workers, having a thorax resembling that of a true queen but being wingless like a worker, and of an intermediate stature. They are of little functional value in either role, being lazy, cowardly, and inefficient and constituting an additional drain on the resources of the colony.

It is possible for vigorous ant colonies to be infested for a number of years without producing these pseudogynes. Eventually, however, as the margin of colonial vitality decreases, they begin to appear. They become increasingly numerous, forming 5, 10, 20 per cent of the colony personnel, and eventually perhaps increasing to as high as 80 per cent of the population. The drain upon the remaining able workers, burdened as they are with the care of the parasite adults and young, their own helpless pseudogyne sisters, and their much-neglected brood, increases. At last the strain becomes too severe and the colony disintegrates, vanquished by the subtle and insidious parasite which it has so long cherished in its midst.

The effect of this parasitism both upon the parasite and upon its host is remarkable in several particulars. It also vividly suggests a convergence of the role of the social parasite and that of a true member of the society. The invader is of course well adapted in a general way to live within the ant community. This is the usual position of a specialized social parasite. But more significant is the fact that it has learned actually to beg food from its hosts by motions of its antennae. Both the adults and the larvae of the beetle are therefore recognized by the ants as true members of their own group, although considered as immature ones, and are given the standard treatment accorded to their own larvae. The parasites are fed by mouth like ant larvae. They are carried about the nest like immature ant forms, and are hustled out of harm's way if danger threatens. The alien has actually attained some status as an individual within the ant society, though only on an infantile basis.

In an allied beetle genus—*Xenodusa*, an American relative of the European *Lomechusa*—this relation has gone further. It too infests ant colonies as an insidious parasite, eventually inducing the production of pseudogynes and probably bringing ultimate destruction on the colony. But this beetle is not content merely to solicit food from its hosts with the antennae alone or to be treated like a larva. Instead, it has learned to imitate closely all the signals —including characteristic movements of the head and forefeet— which adult ants use in begging food from one another. Thus in a very real sense it has mastered an important portion of the sign vocabulary of the colony, and has earned the treatment of an adult and equal. The beetle larvae also solicit food from their nurses after the manner of ant adults, and are likewise treated as adults and equals. Thus the species has taken its place as an integral part of the colony, with full recognition in the framework of the society, notwithstanding the fact that it is viciously inimical to it and even threatens its very existence.

Examples of this assumption by the parasite of the role of a true member of a community are frequent at the level of the individual many-celled organism. There is the familiar case of the nest-parasitism of the European cuckoo and the American cowbirds. This involves a successful exploitation by the parasitic nestling of the brood-tending instincts of the parent birds of the host through the nestling's imitation of the soliciting behavior of the warbler or fly-catcher young.

Thus the evolutionary paths of the parasite and of the social individual may converge in striking fashion. Their structural and functional complexity is often reduced, and specialization and simplification supervene. Apparently there are elements about a society which resemble those of a host environment; the individual in a society behaves in many ways like a parasite. Both are transformed into more dependent entities than are their free-living relatives. But it would be quite wrong to conclude that the individual is merely a social parasite. Its role is far more subtle and complex.

Most parasitic species are dependent upon a particular host only for a portion of the life cycle. They can shift to new hosts more or less readily. This is true of a large proportion of the internal insect parasites, in which the adult is non-parasitic. The same thing is true even of such abjectly dependent internal parasites as the tapeworm, in which, although the worm may finally kill its host and will then itself perish, it will first have shed eggs capable of existing outside the host body, which will eventually be picked up by new hosts.

In all these cases the indefinite survival of any individual host is a matter of comparative indifference to the parasite species. To be sure, the parasite must take care that the host persists long enough for its purposes. Thus those insect larvae which are internally parasitic on various other insect hosts commonly avoid damaging the vital centers in their borings until very nearly the end of their parasitic period. But even the most perfectly evolved systems of apparently obligatory parasitism are relatively loose associations, and even the most specialized of parasites is, in a racial sense, a moderately independent bit of life.

In sharp contrast, the individual within a social group is in quite a different position. Here, although in many senses the individual component is a parasite on the group, it also *is* the group. Thus the group and the individuals composing it are in one sense identities and are absolutely mutually dependent. If a highly specialized worker bee or ant is entirely dependent upon the hive or colony for its continued existence and cannot leave it to enter another, so likewise the colony could not continue if its workers were to desert in numbers. In all true societies the welfare of the individual and of the group are unequivocally identified. The more highly integrated the society and the more thoroughly the individuality of its components has been subordinated to it, the more pointedly is this true.

This poses problems far greater for the individual than for the parasite. In one sense the individual can be a parasite, and can undergo simplification of structure and function in many respects. But, while many of the selective forces which act on the individual strictly within its group may not be so different from those affecting the parasite, those which operate on the group as a whole are essentially like the conditions faced by any independent living entity in the course of its evolution. They in turn lay upon the individual an inescapable obligation to promote the survival of its society in a positive fashion, and to co-operate with its fellows to this end in subtle ways. The role of the individual may be specialized, but it is also functional, and the ultimate criterion which will determine its survival in evolution will be the degree of its usefulness to the whole of which it is a part.

The individuals in a society can frequently be seen to behave in accordance with this demand. Thus they may often actively usurp the positions of those components which have become relatively functionless, or may even eliminate them. It is this which makes the evolution of the imitative lomechusine beetles so remarkable. For although they are wholly inimical to the societies which they parasitize, they have escaped the usual fate which overtakes such intruders in other communities by simulating the appearance of true members of the society so successfully that they can pass for them.

The individual in a society is thus subjected to at least two dissimilar sets of selectional forces. As societies become more closely integrated, the evolution of the individuals composing them may progress in two quite different directions. On the one hand, they may show many degenerative simplifications corresponding to those of the permanent parasites. On the other, they may show specialized complications of structure and function and an increasing perfection of adaptation which will exceed that of their solitary analogues.

Examples of this are abundant and conspicuous. It is a commonplace conjecture that the brain of man has increased greatly in complexity of both structure and function in the course of his social evolution. It is not impossible that such a development is continuing even today. Certainly the brain of modern man exceeds in size and intricacy that of his Neanderthal and Piltdown predecessors, and while it is impossible to demonstrate that his brain is superior to that of so nearly related and comparatively so modern a form as Cro-Magnon man, there can be little question that it exceeds the mind of even that magnificent race in complexity of function.

An analogous case can be traced among the social insects. The brain is relatively highly developed in all hymenopterous insects, solitary and social, and is the center of numerous nerve tracts connecting it with the various sensory organs. The points of entry of these channels are concentrated in two symmetrically placed areas of the brain which can be distinguished quite sharply from the rest of the nervous tissue, and which from their general shape are termed the mushroom bodies. It appears to be principally within these bodies that the resolution, integration, and co-ordination of the sensory impressions take place, and the impulses which will guide the often complex responses to these stimuli are apparently also generated here. The mushroom bodies are thus in some ways analogous to the human forebrain, and they are very probably the seat of whatever psychic impressions a social insect may have. These, it is to be emphasized, are probably not remotely comparable with human consciousness.

Now the human forebrain has shown the greatest relative increase in size of any part of the brain in the course of evolution, and it is interesting to observe that a similar enlargement of the mushroom bodies has taken place among the social, as compared with the solitary, hymenopterous insects. The relatively least developed condition is that of the sawflies and horntails—solitary dwellers of the trees with independent, leaf-feeding larvae that resemble butterfly caterpillars—which are the most primitive of all. At the other extreme, the mushroom bodies attain their greatest size and complexity among the social wasps, bees, and ants, while the solitary wasps and bees are intermediate. This corresponds to the increased complexity of the instinct endowment which takes place with socialization and permits of the complex nest, brood, and interpersonnel relations of these communal insects.

In human civilization a specialization of the individual to his role appears in an incipient form as early as communal living. Among the Australian aborigines the specialization of the sexes in respect to food-gathering is already well advanced. It seems probable that this adaptation of the male to hunting and warfare, and of the female to occupations of daily support for the group, appeared in many ancient paleolithic tribes. With the rise of more elaborate techniques, such as stock tending and agriculture, this specialization deepened. As the activities broadened, any one of them could only be adequately mastered by the devotion of more and more attention to it throughout the life of the worker.

At some time early in the typical history of peoples there has come another sort of specialization of even greater significance. This is the craft of the magician and the medicine man. In many groups it appears that these two were able not only to dominate the groups in which they appeared, at least partly by virtue of their skill in exploiting the fear of the unknown, but also to take the extraordinarily significant step of providing a specialty in the community life not immediately concerned with food getting. Here, perhaps for the first time, was a profession which had to be supported but which contributed nothing directly to the sustenance of the community. In the truest sense, it was a luxury—an extra drain which had to be met from the surplus resources that the fortune, skill, and degree of integration of the community had enabled it to put away. Thus the typical medicine man must early have assumed a role analogous in some respects to that of certain of the mouthless hydranths of the Portuguese man-of-war and in other ways suggestive of the beetle parasite which, through the sensory fascination it exerts on the members of an ant colony, subsists on the reserves of food which the energy and organization of the community have accumulated. Such a role as that of the medicine man easily shifts to that of pure social parasite. How often this shift has been actually effected is attested in our knowledge of the behavior of primitive, and sometimes of more advanced, peoples.

When metal replaced stone for weapons, tools, and ornamental purposes, another significant craft specialization probably supervened. For Neolithic peoples metal working was with little question an intricate and difficult art. Unlike the simpler crafts of pottery manufacture or weaving, it could not be mastered by the whole group, but only by a select few, who thus came to form a skilled craft group. Such groups are conspicuous even among Stone Age peoples. The Tasmanian race were in some ways perhaps the most primitive living people that have been observed; yet even here the work in the stone pits was of a somewhat specialized character. In higher stone cultures, such as those of the early North American Indians, the arrow makers and the fashioners of exquisitely chipped and balanced spears and axheads were a professional class, with a very special place in the tribal organization, while the Neolithic flint miners of England and Sweden had already, apparently, built up a specialized industry.

With the use of copper implements this rift probably deepened. The mysteries of the copper workers must have been far removed from the craft knowledge of the common people. There is some evidence that the copper worker, like the medicine man, did his best to preserve and even to widen this gulf by the addition of superfluous mysteries, probably in the interest of his own social prestige. Furthermore, the copper worker, again like the medicine man, was far removed from the sphere of food gathering. Although the tools which he made might be deemed of great service in the business of survival, yet while he was producing them he could not be an effective hunter and must be fed by the community. He had lost his economic self-sufficiency and his sphere of activity had become sharpened and narrowed, again like the specialized hydranth of the siphonophoran colony.

The copper worker well typifies another important development in specialization. The loss of his self-sufficiency had also helped to destroy the self-sufficiency of the other members of his community, and had gone a long way toward converting the community itself into a closely integrated organization of mutually interdependent parts. For ultimately it must have become apparent that in combat stone knives could not compete with copper knives and that a wooden plow was no match for one of metal when the soil must be turned ever more deeply as it became exhausted. Copper was then no longer a mere luxury. It had become a necessity. The community had become dependent upon the metalworker no less than he was dependent upon it. Soon the demand for copper implements must have far exceeded the supply which any one man could turn out. And so there came the itinerant metalworkers, forerunner of the tinkers of today. Such metalworkers, traveling with their ingots from village to village and hammering out tools to order, apparently had an important place in widely separated areas of the world among peoples just emerging from the late Stone Age.

Once this stage of communal specialization was reached in a given culture, through whatever crafts, it is clear that human civilization had entered a critical phase of evolution suggestive of the missing link in the organic evolution of integrated biological societies. Competition between communities probably became severe. Increased organization and internal integration, with its accompanying heightened specialization, may often have been the price of survival for a communal entity. In Sumeria between 2000 and 3000 B.C., bakers, brewers, spinners, weavers, animal breeders, clerks, priests, cultivators, glaziers, jewelers, seal cutters, government officials, all constituted strictly specialized professions and all were organized into working societies under the aegis of the temples of the prevailing religion. The members of each profession gave their full time to their specialized tasks, and the organization of their working groups gave them security as to food and shelter. But it also robbed them of much of their earlier individual independence, stole much of their freedom, and narrowed their sphere of generalized action. By Hellenistic times specialized industries of many sorts had been developed, and craftsmen were immutably fixed to their tasks. In Greek Delos of 100 b.c., the joiner whose proper trade it was to fit doors could not set up the doorposts for them; this was the task of another group of professionals.

A stage suggestive of that of modern trade union organization had been reached. To such a degree had the specialization of the individual to his society gone even at a relatively early stage of human social evolution. How much more pronounced, in certain aspects, is the problem before us today!

CHAPTER 6

The Society as Parasite and the Institution of Slavery

THE CONCEPT of parasitism can be extended well beyond the situation where one individual is parasitic on another or on a society. Whole groups or societies can themselves become parasitic units. When they do they exhibit much the same degenerative and specialized changes in evolution as those that characterize the individual parasite. This parasitism of groups is common in the social history of men. An excellent case in point is the situation in Spain in the seventeenth and eighteenth centuries, when her social structure had become so burdened with nonproductive groups within the body politic that national functions were gravely impaired. From 1570 to 1620 the number of Spanish monasteries, which did not contribute very directly to the welfare of the state, trebled, and the number of mendicant friars in the time of Philip III totaled over 30,000. In 1788 approximately a third of the population was listed in the priestly or government servant groups. In addition, there was a vast army of unproductive beggars and vagabonds who lived frankly at the expense of the body politic. All this may have been an important factor in Spain's decline as a world power. Other examples of human social parasitism come readily to mind—the parasitism of the courtier class of Louis XIV of France, that of the *daimio* of Japan in the time of the Tokugawa Shoguns, and the parasitism of caste in old India.

While some of these relationships have left marks upon society which may be permanent, group parasitism in man has not been of first importance in his social evolution. The reason may lie in part in the fact that this evolution is so recent. In part it may be because of man's relatively high intolerance of such imposition. It is quite otherwise among the social insects. Here social parasitism of the most striking kind has been anciently established and long perpetuated. Often these relationships have involved extraordinary specialization.

Close examination of the nests of a certain American yellow jacket—*Vespa diabolica*—at the height of the summer season but before the young males and queens of the new generation have appeared may disclose a curious fact. In some there may appear, not the single queen typically found, but two. Closely similar in appearance and behavior, both are treated in much the same manner by the workers. Despite their apparent likenesses, however, their histories differ widely. One was the founder of the colony. She it was that, after a winter's hibernation, searched the fields and woods for a suitable location for the nest. She spent long hours scraping logs and fence posts for their wood pulp and macerating it into paper to fashion the first little tier of cells, whose envelope looked like a gray and fragile golf ball. Here the first broods of workers were brought to maturity and the colony was launched upon its existence. Thereafter the founder spent most of her time within the nest, rarely if ever again venturing upon the wing.

The other queen has a quite dissimilar background. She too hibernated and also emerged with spring to make searching flights in the pastures and the woodlands. But the object of her quest was different. She was seeking, not an appropriate site for a colony, but rather a yellow-jacket community already in an incipient stage of development. When she found such a nest she gained entry to the citadel, usually most effectively guarded, and secured adoption by the worker personnel, normally hostile to any intruder. As the weeks passed, this newcomer began to lay eggs in the cells of the comb. The resulting alien young were raised by the yellow-jacket workers. At maturity they proved to be, not workers of *Vespa diabolica*, but instead perfect queens and males, of an entirely different, parasitic species, *Vespa arctica*, in which the worker caste is wholly lacking. After a brief period of idleness they left the nest for good. Throughout their whole existence in the colony, this intruding parasite queen and her progeny drew constantly on their yellow-jacket hosts for care and sustenance. Nothing was ever returned.

There is a bumblebee of the New England states—*Psithyrus laboriosus*—which has similar parasitic habits.

Here again the species lacks the worker form. After emerging from hibernation, the perfect female spends the last of May and often most of June searching for a suitable young host colony of bumblebees of the species *Bombus vagans* or *Bombus impatiens*. Having located such a community, the would-be parasite enters by a combination of stealth and outright brigandage. Frequently she seizes the small but spirited workers of the host species and rolls them under her body so roughly that they become intimidated and do not attempt further resistance. Rarely, however, does she sting or severely injure them, for they will be badly needed in the future colonial economy, upon which she is about to become wholly dependent.

After a few days the intruding queen is accepted by the workers, and usually also by their queen-mother. There are no further hostilities, and the now mixed community settles down to the routine of its economy. As soon as this has occurred, the guest proceeds to tear open the brood cells of her host, rolling the eggs and the larvae which they contain out onto the floor of the nest. No bumblebee recognizes any object—not even its own egg or larva—lying on the nest floor away from the cells as anything but debris. Accordingly, the *Bombus* workers quickly gather up their own dispossessed young, carry them outside, and throw them away. The guest queen then constructs new brood cells from the materials of the ruined comb and deposits her own eggs therein. The care of them is promptly taken over by the community nurses. When they hatch they are faithfully reared to maturity, emerging as males and young queens of the parasites. During August and September a constant stream of young parasitic males and queens is produced. Then, like the mature young of the parasitic wasps, shortly thereafter they leave the community permanently, and contribute nothing to its support.

In these associations the invader queen, once her position in the nest is fully recognized, does not molest her opposite member, and the two live peacefully side by side. However, any rival *Psithyrus* which subsequently seeks to enter this host colony is promptly evicted or actually killed by the parasite already in residence. A young bumblebee community can normally support but one outside female and her progeny, and the parasite takes good care that its host shall not be overburdened.

Many other instances of similar parasitism are known among the wasps and bees. In each case the parasitic species has lost its worker caste and has ceased to be a typically social insect. In each case likewise the host species has retained that caste, and has continued to be social. Thus the trend to simplicity has been plainly evident in the evolution of these parasitic societies, but not of their hosts. So alike in other respects are many of the parasites and their hosts that it seems quite likely that the parasite has been actually derived from its host in evolution. Like many other parasites—such as specific diseases, for example—a given parasite typically infests one and only one species of host.

Paleontology furnishes no positive proof that a worker caste was ever developed in the evolution of these parasitic bees and wasps. Yet the circumstantial evidence from their structure and their relationships indicates strongly that the present elementary condition of their societies, with its lack of any worker caste, represents a secondary return from a more complex to a simpler state concomitant with their parasitic mode of life. In the absence of a contrary indication, one is almost forced to accept this concept.

A study of social parasitism among the ants gives very strong support to this conclusion. Here beautiful living series are available which illustrate successive stages of a progressive reduction in function of the worker caste and the simplification of colonial structure attendant upon the parasitic mode of life in societies no less than in individuals. This situation culminates in forms where, as among the parasitic wasps and bees, the worker caste has entirely disappeared. Among certain ants, it seems quite clear that the workerless, permanently parasitic species have been derived in evolution from once independent social forms in which the worker caste was functional and fully represented.

Among the ants native to the fields and woodlands of our eastern states several examples can be found of the first stages of this trend. Notable among them are *Formica difficilis,* and *Aphaenogaster tennesseensis.* The queen of the latter is actually smaller than her own workers, in striking contrast to the bulky queens usual to other members of this genus. Smooth, shining, slippery, and crafty, she is well fitted to enter an alien colony by stealth, but she is ill provisioned indeed to go out and establish an independent colony of her own. After the nuptial flight and the descent to earth she casts her wings in typical ant fashion and at once begins a feverish search. Her objective is not a likely depression in which to build a nest. Rather it is to locate some suitable community of her prospective host—a closely related species with large queens which establish their colonies in normal fashion. Having found such a nest, the invader approaches it cautiously and, at an appropriate moment, slips within. She may meet with some resistance from the alien worker personnel, but her small size and slippery surface and possibly, also, a neutral odor, all conspire to make her inconspicuous and difficult to catch. In a short time she is accepted by the workers.

The course of events after this is somewhat clouded. The host-queen apparently perishes shortly after the entrance of the invader, and it is possible that she is assassinated by the intruder. Considering the relative weakness and the small stature of the latter, however, it seems more likely that she is regularly eliminated by her own perverted workers in favor of the parasite. In any case, the intruder then settles down quietly to lay numbers of eggs. These are faithfully adopted and nurtured by the foster nurses. Unlike the situation with the parasitic wasps and bees, these young at maturity prove to be perfectly normal workers, in some ways more like the workers of the host than like their own mother. They assume a full share of the burden of colony maintenance and assist their hosts in all the normal domestic duties. As time goes on, more and more vigorous young alien workers appear while the aging native workers die off, until ultimately there is left a pure and prosperous community of the aliens.

Then it is, normally, that the colony rids itself of the last remaining stigma of its parasitic origin by a significant mass move to a new home. Mature colonies of *Aphaenogaster tennesseensis* are commonly found in wet decaying logs on the forest floor. This is clearly their preferred habitat. The host, on the other hand, is normally a soil-nesting species, placing its colonies by preference under stones in the mold at the edge of woodlands, a favorite habitat being under stone walls. The parasite must perforce accept these conditions at first, and young communities are usually found in such locations. But with the coming of maturity and the final assumption of independence the move to wood is accomplished. Thereafter the once parasitic colony may persist for many years as a thriving independent entity. Save in the bodily structure of its queen, there is no hint of its parasitic origin.

This is essentially the first stage in the evolution of social parasitism among ants. So far, it has been reflected in the physical characteristics of the queen and in the mode of foundation of the colony. It has brought little change in the permanent structure of the mature community. In another and more spectacular social parasite the relation has been carried further, and there has been additional specialization of the female to her curious role.

The young queen of this parasite—*Bothriomyrmex decapitans* —approaches with great circumspection the nest of the host species which she seeks to enter. Permitting herself to be attacked near the entrance, she is seized and dragged back and forth across the crater by the excited and at first hostile owners. Sooner or later, if the invading queen has not actually been pulled inside the nest in this tumult, she seizes an opportunity to dart within. There she takes refuge on a pile of brood, where she will be fairly safe from attack. As soon as the excitement has died down and the coast is clear, she seeks out the host queen. Firmly attaching herself, she rides on the back of this host female, sometimes for days. During this period her chief activity consists in vigorously sawing off the head of the queen from above. This accomplished she takes over the colony and lays numerous eggs which are adopted by the host workers. Thenceforward the mixed community follows a course similar to that of *Aphaenogaster*. The end result is a pure nest of the guest ants which gives little hint of its parasitic origin.

A further stage in this evolution is illustrated in another group of ants. Here the society never achieves independence, but remains parasitic throughout its existence. Concomitantly, the worker caste of the species has become much altered and seems to be disappearing. The course of social parasitism in an American species of this group—*Leptothorax provancheri*—is known in considerable detail. It is not uncommon in the southern New England states, where it dwells in boggy meadows in close association with its independently living host, *Myrmica brevinodis*. The guests live between the walls of the nest of the much larger host and maintain continual communication through galleries too small for the host workers to enter. Thus, the guest ants spend much time with the host but receive no return visits. They are warmly welcomed, a condition quite at variance with the usual implacable hostility characteristic of ant colonies even of the same species. They spend much time licking and grooming their hosts. In return they are liberally fed. In consequence of these easy and constant sources of nourishment, the guest workers are seldom required to go outside the confines of their own nest and that of their host or to forage independently for food. The community as a whole is permanently dependent—a protected, internal parasite on the "tissues," so to speak, of its host.

The modifications of the parasitic society which accompany this mode of life are marked. The worker caste in the guest colony appears to be well on its way to disappearance—by disintegration, as it were. Nearly all of the workers have some of the physical characteristics of the queens of the species, having well-developed ovaries and laying eggs freely. These intermediate queen-workers are so abundant that it is not hard to imagine that in time the true worker caste may disappear, leaving only perfect females and males to represent the species. The climax in this simplification of social structure has been reached among permanently parasitic types of ants. Here the worker caste has wholly disappeared. In the less specialized of these forms—*Wheeleriella, Epoecus,* and *Sympheidole*—although the worker class has vanished, the structure of the males and the perfect females is but little modified from the normal. Unlike all the social ant parasites so far considered, however, the first-generation larvae of these ants mature as males and queens, which shortly leave the colony. The establishment of any permanent social structure by the intruder is therefore out of the question, and the parasitic queen must perish with the death of the host workers in existence at the time of her entry.

In the most specialized of the workerless social parasites, such as the European *Anergates atratulus,* both the queen and the male ants have undergone degenerative bodily changes and bear most strikingly the marks of their mode of life. The male is not only wingless; he is so torpid and helpless that he is unable to leave the parent nest or to participate in any but the most rudimentary activities. While any semblance of a nuptial flight is thus impossible, the small winged females, after mating with their brothers within the nests of their birth, do emerge and engage in a dispersion flight. On descending they remove their wings and seek out colonies of their characteristic host species. As soon as they have gained entry and become established, they undergo specialized and degenerative bodily changes. The abdomen and ovaries swell enormously, and the queens gradually become transformed into egg-laying machines of vast fecundity. At the same time they grow sluggish and almost helpless. Like so many mature tapeworms, they are entirely devoted to producing as many offspring as possible before the host colonies shall die and the evanescent chance of race survival be irrevocably lost.

In these workerless and degenerate guest ants, as in the workerless guest wasps and bees, is illustrated the extreme of simplification of the parasite society.

Despite the divergent origin and evolution of these parasitic insect societies, certain characteristics are common to them. By these they are sharply set apart from related independent forms. The first is the highly specific relation which has evolved between the parasite and its host. This parasitic relationship of guest and host is characteristic of the yellow jackets, the bumblebees, and the ants alike. In each case, the parasite and the host species are rather nearly allied in point of classification.

A second striking characteristic common to the social parasites is the high fecundity of their females. All of them are prolific, some to an extraordinary degree. Despite this, however, these parasitic wasps and bees are comparatively rare creatures, and some of the parasitic ants are so scarce that they have been found on only a few occasions. This situation probably results from the extraordinary hazards attending the initial establishment of the young queens in their host communities. On the other hand, the host species are without exception common, widespread, and vigorous insects which range widely over the territory where the parasites occur.

But the most conspicuous and interesting common characteristic is that of the simplification of social structure through the evolutionary loss of various features. This becomes progressively more evident as the parasitic habit becomes established and deepened. In several cases, this trend extends beyond the level of the community structure and is to be seen in the structure of the individual itself. Witness the wingless condition of some of the male ants and the marked reduction in size, the loss of available fat and of wing muscles, and the specialization and simplification of the

brood instincts of the queens. In all their bodily features these females are more nearly reminiscent of the primitive ants, in which
the stature of queen and worker is nearly equal. Yet it is evident
that their condition is not a primitive one, but represents a return
to the simpler state.

One more point in this relationship is worth noticing. With
very few exceptions the simplification so often exemplified in the
social parasite leaves its host virtually untouched. In these partner-
ships it is the exploiter, not the victim, which becomes the dependent, undergoes losses of function, and gradually sacrifices
various structures which make independent living possible. The
host which carries its double burden may suffer individually—
may even perish. But its species goes its way unmodified and
unaffected in the larger aspects of its evolutionary course by this
imposed relation.

The Institution of Slavery

These consequences of social parasitism are vividly exemplified in a special situation which is closely akin to it. The ultimate
expression of this fascinating aspect of parasitism has poignant
implications for the case of man. This institution is, in a word—
slavery.

The simplest condition of slavery is that in which one individual employs another for its own use or to do its bidding, with
no reciprocal benefit. Typical of this situation in nature is the practice of a little crab—*Melia*—which lacks the powerful pincers
of many of its relatives. In their place it carries in its two small
claws a pair of sea anemones, which are used as living instruments
in self-defense and possibly in capturing its prey. But a far more
vivid illustration is to be found at the level of the society, in a living
series which exemplifies the evolution of slavery among ants.

The first example is offered by the ant *Formica rufa*—one of
the conspicuous denizens of European forests. Its huge colonies

are housed in great thatched mounds which never fail to attract attention. This unusually aggressive ant possesses great independence of action. It is partly carnivorous in habit, hunting out and destroying much of the insect life over a large area about the nest. Long ago it discovered the succulent and abundant food supply readily available in the fat larvae and pupae of colonies of weaker species of closely related ants. Its specialty is raiding the nests of other ants of the same genus and carrying off great quantities of their larvae and pupae as food for its own young.

These stolen pupae are commonly stored in a living condition until they are needed. Inevitably a few of them ultimately mature into young adults. These individuals, born in the center of a foreign community and knowing no other environment, settle down without protest as auxiliary members of the alien colony. It is not uncommon to find nests containing numbers of them. They play a minor and ancillary, but nevertheless an appreciable, part in colonial activities.

The next stage in this evolution is represented by a red-and-black ant—*Formica sanguinea*—which forms conspicuous nests in the fields and on the edges of woodlands in our northern states. Like *Formica rufa*, it also preys on other ants to rob them of their larvae and pupae, but here the relation has become more specialized. The raids are usually confined to a single related black species or its subspecies, including our common black pavement ants. Such forays are well organized and are undertaken in concert by nearly all the members of the raiding colony, for the specific purpose of obtaining large numbers of the black young. At rather regular intervals during the summer—usually early in the afternoon—a great crowd of workers assembles about the crater of the nest. As soon as the army has formed, it sets off in a long column toward the potential slave colony, which may be situated as much as an eighth of a mile away.

On arriving at the mound the raiders plunge into the community. The invader is a more powerful and aggressive type than its victims. Usually the latter flee, leaving their brood pile unguarded. Not infrequently, however, they put up some resistance, when they are met with ruthless savagery. Within a few minutes each of the invaders secures a larva or pupa and leaves the nest. The column straggles homeward, laden with booty, in looser and more open formation than when it went out.

The object of the raid is to secure the young of the victims, but not, as in the case of *Formica rufa*, primarily for food. They are employed for a more specific and long-range purpose. A few of them are doubtless eaten, but the great majority are reared to maturity. Knowing no other environment, they settle down as effective workers in their adopted colony. They aid in excavating the nest, in caring for the queen and the adult workers, and in rearing the brood. They do not participate in the subsequent slave-raiding procedures but give especial attention to receiving and rearing to maturity the captured young of their own species. They are highly useful aids to their captors, but, ant for ant, they are no individual match for them. When any major shift in the location of the community is to be made the slaveholders design and execute the move. Then the slaves are actually carried to the new site by their mistresses. It is thus the captors which really determine the major factors in the life of the community. The captives are able auxiliaries, but their function in the economy is reminiscent in many ways of that of the slaves in the plantation economy of the old South.

In the next stage of this evolution, the relationship between slaves and slaveholder is virtually reversed. This is illustrated by a beautiful blood-red ant—*Polyergus lucidus*—native to our northeastern states, and ranging as far westward as the Rocky Mountains and well south toward the Gulf. It too is a slaveholder, but it characteristically selects as its slaves the members of a different group of *Formica* species.

Polyergus is a specialized warrior and nothing else. In its forays a compact army masses at the top of the nest. Thereupon, closely assembled as though at command, a close-knit, well-oriented column sets out on its mission. Arriving at the nest of the victims, the army enters, still in a comparatively disciplined fashion. The inmates are timid ants, and normally they simply scatter into the grass, abandoning everything to the invaders. Indeed, colonies that have been raided two or three times during the summer may become so sensitive that they will evacuate the nest and flee at the mere approach of an invading column when it is still at a considerable distance.

If the slave colony is a populous one, however, and has not been previously stormed, it may offer some resistance. In such case the invaders take effective action. Their mandibles, unlike those of most related ants, have lost the characteristic toothing which serves so usefully in the daily tasks of foraging and nest-care. Instead, they have become sickle-shaped and sharply pointed scimitars, beautifully adapted to piercing the crania of the slave species. If any prospective victim is so bold as to seize a larva or pupa and attempt to escape, it is met by a *Polyergus* which seizes its head in its sickle-shaped mandibles. The attacker may at first apply only gentle pressure—a firm hint as to the course of action to be followed. If the larva or pupa is promptly released, the captive adult may escape. If not, the mandibles meet, the worker crumples, and the larva or pupa is picked up by the aggressor.

When most of the members of the raiding column have acquired a kidnaped larva or pupa, the army reassembles and returns home. Here it is met by the slaves already resident in the *Polyergus* colony, which at once relieve the warrior mistresses of the booty, and take all further care of it. Within the nest the slave-holders live in virtually complete idleness. They take no part in excavation, in foraging for food, or in caring for either their own or the slave young. They are even fed by the slaves, becoming so specialized and helpless that even in the presence of abundant food they will die of starvation in the absence of their keepers. If the nest site is to be changed, it is the slaves which select the new location, excavate the new nest, and carry the passive mistresses into it. This is the exact reverse of the procedure in the two preceding cases, those of *Formica rufa* and *Formica sanguinea*.

The red-and-black ant—*Formica sanguinea*—is not necessarily dependent upon its auxiliaries. Many prosperous communities may be found that are entirely free of them—indeed, some of its subspecies characteristically maintain no slaves in their mature communities. But *Polyergus* cannot exist away from its slaves, and no colonies have ever been found without them. Again, even in slaveholding *sanguinea* colonies, the population of slaveholders usually exceeds the number of slaves. Here that relation is reversed —for if the mistresses constitute a wholly warrior caste, it requires a large auxiliary population to support them. This is the dangerous extent to which the evolution of slavery has gone in its effect upon the slaveholder.

Both *Formica* and *Polyergus* belong to the same subfamily and are rather closely related. It is entirely possible that they may be directly linked in evolution. This is not the case with the next example in the series, which illustrates admirably a further stage in the evolution of slavery. This ant—*Strongylognathus huberi*—is a rather small European and African insect of wide but spotty distribution. Its colonies always contain numerous slaves of a single species—a common European pavement ant, *Tetramorium caespitum.* The workers of the slaveholding colony have similar toothless, falcate mandibles, well adapted to warfare, although it is questionable whether their muscles are still strong enough to allow them to pierce the heads of their victims. Nevertheless, they threaten vigorously, and apparently effectively. They seem still to make abortive raids upon their slave species. In the case of a Swiss mountain form—*alpinus*—it is known that these forays differ from those of *Formica* and *Polyergus* in that the slaves accompany the mistresses on their nocturnal raids and do most of the work of plundering and despoiling the alien colony of their own species. The slaveholding workers take no interest in the care of the brood or in the excavation of the nest and play a wholly minor part in the social economy.

The final step in the development of slavery makes the slaveholder truly a parasite of the slave. In the species *Strongylognathus testaceus* the instinct of raiding seems to have been wholly lost. The workers still possess the familiar sickle-shaped mandibles, but their muscles are so weak that they can no longer make even an effective pretense of aggression. Despite these infirmities, these ants still dwell in thriving communities of their slaves, *Tetramorium caespitum*. Here they are much at home, though they play no essential part in the colonial economy. Strikingly enough, such communities may contain living and healthy "slave" queens. The brood of both species is reared simultaneously, the slave workers toiling faithfully in bringing up the young of the perfectly useless intruders, which are now reduced to a position of abject dependence.

Here, as can be readily seen, the evolution of slavery converges on that of the workerless parasites. Indeed, the whole development of slavery among ants is, in a subtle way, simply a modified example of the evolution of parasitism. Like parasites, the slaveholders gradually become more and more the dependents of the slaves. Most of the criteria which distinguish social parasitism apply also to the case of slavery. As among the true parasites, the slaveholders, in all the further evolutionary stages, are of uncommon and sporadic occurrence. Only the red-and-black ants—*Formica sanguinea* —among which the institution of slaveholding is in its relative infancy, are vigorous and abundant today. On the other hand, the slave or host types are all widely distributed, common species. Likewise, as with the social parasites, the predilection of each slaveholder for a particular species of slave is highly critical and constant. As with the parasitic forms, again, the slaveholding and the slave species are characteristically rather closely related.

The convergence of slavery toward parasitism of the slaveholder is even more vividly emphasized by the methods of colony foundation practiced by the slaveholding species, at the time when their colonial economy is weakest. None of the queens of the slaveholding species found their communities independently. All of them rely for assistance upon the alien species from which they will later draw their slaves. After the young queen has flown, descended to earth, and discarded her wings, she seeks out weak or incipient colonies of the slave species peculiar to her. Having found such a nest, she enters, essentially by force. She makes at once for the brood pile and captures as many of the mature larvae and pupae as possible, intimidating or killing the rightful owners. She then retires into a small cell with her nearly grown booty, which requires virtually no feeding and only a little care before mature worker ants of the slave species appear.

As soon as this occurs the young slave ants adopt the queen and proceed to forage and care for her. She then lays eggs which the young slaves rear, and a mixed colony results. As soon as the maturing workers are sufficiently strong in numbers, they organize raids on other communities of the characteristic auxiliary species to perpetuate the supply. And so the relation continues, with periodic artificial replenishment of slave personnel, throughout the life of the slaveholding colony. In those instances in which the nest at maturity contains no slaves, the raiding instinct of the young community lapses early in its development, there is no fresh supply of auxiliaries, and the colony becomes pure and wholly independent.

This behavior of the youthful queens differs from that of the young females of a social parasite such as *Aphaenogaster tennesseensis* in only one or two essential details, though these are significant. The queens of the slaveholders seek out very young communities of their hosts in preference to the larger, better-established colonies sought by the parasitic ant. The slaveholding queens overcome the adult members of these weak communities by force, acquire the brood by brigandage, and make no attempt to secure acceptance by the adult and presumably irreconcilable colony personnel. This contrasts rather sharply with the more subtle method by which the parasitic ants secure adoption by the adult workers of the colonies which they invade. Finally, the workers of the slaveholders, unlike those of the parasite, toil actively to keep the slave supply fresh—with the exception of those subspecies of *sanguinea* which do not keep slaves at colonial maturity—so that the colony neither becomes pure (like *Aphaenogaster*) nor perishes when the original supply of alien workers dies away (like *Anergates*).

The resemblance of the slaveholders to the true parasites becomes even more striking as one progresses further in the slaveholding series. Little is known of the method of colony foundation of *Strongylognathus huberi,* but the evidence seems good that the young queen, like the young parasite queen, secures adoption in an already established slave colony and contrives either to destroy the rival queen or to bring about her assassination by her own workers. In the final stage—*Strongylognathus testaceus*—the convergence between slavery and parasitism is completed. Here it is certain that the young queen secures adoption into the colony of the host species, since the host queen, which is suffered to live, can actually be found in the nest. The only way in which this slave economy can be distinguished from that of a degenerate parasite is that a few members of the old worker caste still persist, and the host queen, instead of being assassinated, is permitted to reproduce so that the life of the slaveholder is not limited by one generation of the slaves. Were it not for the fact that this last slaveholding species is evidently so closely allied to the species preceding it in the series, in which the slave-raiding instinct persists in abortive form, the former might quite as well be placed in the evolutionary line leading from the social insect to the workerless parasite as in the line leading from slaveholding to the same condition. The convergence of the two lines of evolution to the state of the degenerate workerless parasite seems evident.

It is logical to conclude that slavery is closely akin to social parasitism. This conclusion seems justified despite the high specializations accompanying slavery as an institution and the fact that it has often evolved along lines which tend to obscure that significant relationship. The suggestion is strong that, wherever slavery appears, if it persists and evolves sufficiently, it will take on the same general characteristics, and be subject to much the same limitations, as govern the evolution of parasitism. Further, in such an evolution it will be the slaveholders, not the slaves, that undergo great modification and specialization in consequence of the relation—it will be the well-served masters, not their servants, that will ultimately suffer such simplification as will unfit them for any independent mode of life.

This parallel certainly finds some expression in the case of man. Yet so vast are the sweeps of time in which organic evolution has been going forward that they dwarf the brief existence of the race of man, and give to many qualities of human social evolution an aspect of evanescence. Developments which among other societies and organisms seem long since to have reached a point of equilibrium appear in man to be still dynamic, and in a form where the end is not readily to be seen. This quality of immaturity and impermanence is very characteristic of the institution of social parasitism in human society. Particularly is this true when that society is compared with the ancient, stable, and often fantastically involved developments among various older groups. This same quality distinguishes the institution of human slavery.

The custom of slaveholding is probably as old as the human race. Certainly there are few tribal groups in the world today which do not bear some evidence of the slaveholding habit. None of the great civilizations has been so obliterated that all traces of its slave-keeping customs have disappeared. In Sumeria, in Babylon, in Assyria, in Judea, evidence is abundantly available to attest the practice. In Egypt, above all, the memory of a vast slave system is timelessly enthroned in the great Pyramids which could never have been erected without the pitiless exploitation of countless auxiliaries.

In many hunting economies, such as those of the Indians of the American Northwest, slaves were in constant demand as paddlers for the great war canoes, and their performance of menial domestic functions made possible the release of a portion of the fighting potential of the tribe. This type of slavery is a relatively unspecialized one. In such a community the social position of the slave, while undoubtedly inferior and underprivileged, does not seem to have been greatly different from that of his master. The difference was that the mean, the routine, and the inglorious tasks were consistently his lot, and he it was whose life was sacrificed in the event of any communal crisis. Among slightly more advanced societies, however, the position of the slave may become more specialized and more depressed.

This specialization can proceed along several lines. One of the most interesting is the direction which it tends to take among nomadic, herding peoples at the time when their conquests have been so successful that a large potential slave population has fallen captive to their sword. Functional specialization has already proceeded far among herding nomads. Generations of cattle tending have evolved an economy which is well adjusted to its very special environment. The relationship is essentially that between the cattle as givers of milk and meat on the one hand, and on the other their human guardians, who drive them from pasture to pasture as the grass withers and from water to water as the droughts come, and protect their young from the attacks of wild animals—in short, husband them and secure their increase.

When a nomad society of this kind enters upon widespread depredations, sooner or later it finds itself in regions of cultivated fields and established cities with a vast number of human captives at hand. The new land may compel a precipitate abandonment of the old way of life, for in such situations the keeping of cattle may be highly uneconomical. But this people from the grasslands is practically a stranger to the techniques of extracting a living from the soil. Even more is it a stranger to the ways of cities. As a result, it may seek to substitute the conquered human population for its cattle. In place of keeping herds of cattle on which it can subsist directly, it can now keep herds of human slaves, on whose agricultural labor it can subsist quite as effectually as if these slaves were being slaughtered and devoured.

This, however, was only a relatively primitive step in the evolution of slavery. Later stages in human history involve not only the employment of the slave class as mass agriculturists, but its further adaptation to a variety of other tasks. Training of the slaves to act as a specialized warrior class was very frequent. The height of specialization may be represented by the slave household of the Ottomans at the peak of their development. Young slaves were closely scrutinized for potential talent, and were trained as scribes, authors, governmental administrators, and soldiers. All these owed to the household or to the state the development of their talents, and were perpetually bound to serve it faithfully. In the intensely specialized individuals that resulted, trained in a system which made a vigorous appeal to ambition and exploited every talent to the utmost, but punished failure ruthlessly and at no time freed the individual for any exercise of his talents other than for the benefit of the alien society, it is probable that there existed as high and as irrevocable a degree of specialization of the individual to the society as may be found among men.

The slavery practiced in the classical world of Greece and Rome exhibits a similar evolution toward the differentiation of the individual. In its early stages Greek slavery was a relatively unspecialized institution. The slave might be of the same race, birth, and breeding as his master, and he was commonly well treated in the household and used more as an auxiliary and a partner than as a servant. A marked change was wrought by the growth of agriculture into a systematized industry, requiring the cultivation of large tracts of land, and the growth of Greek military effort, demanding for armed service every available free citizen.

After the Peloponnesian war the masters of the landed estates became largely absentee owners, leaving the management of their holdings predominantly to their slaves. This led inevitably to mass operations, with their concomitant degrading effects on the great numbers of slaves employed as field laborers, and then to caste specialization of the slaves into workers, proprietors, and managers.

Gradually the specialization of caste was extended, and slave labor penetrated into every phase of Greek communal life. Slaves became artisans, commercial and banking agents, musicians, mine and factory workers, soldiers, and municipal agents. Moreover, each group became more and more pointedly narrowed to its own profession.

This slave specialization was even more marked in Rome. There again slavery began as a relatively inconspicuous and unspecialized institution. During the conquest of the Italian mainland, the source of slaves was mainly captive enemies taken in war. Of much the same race and culture as their captors, they were used by the farmer or householder essentially as junior partners in daily tasks. As Rome developed and her conquests multiplied, and as plantations expanded and industry increased, however, the patrician again came to be habitually an absentee, leaving his estates in the care of specialized slave-overseers who superintended great numbers of field workers. And as no slave master can be so brutal as an overseer who is also a slave, the lot of these workers became progressively worse. At the other extreme, slaves who were more fortunate, intelligent, or energetic attained to important positions. They occupied the lower offices in the law courts, in public works, and in other arenas of municipal function. In private service, the slave community was divided into many occupational grades, including responsible posts of administration, and professional positions such as those of artists, physicians, secretaries and librarians, readers, grammarians, actors, gladiators, and circus performers.

As the Roman state matured, the numbers of its slaves increased until they formed an important sector of the population. In the time of Claudius, it has been estimated, there were in the Roman Empire not less than twenty million slaves.

The completion of the Roman conquest reduced the supply of slaves which until then had been obtained principally in military campaigns or through slave forays into non-Roman territory. Now emphasis was shifted to the propagation of slave children, and increased attention was given to the maintenance of slave families. The results were twofold. On the one hand the condition of the slave was somewhat improved because he had become a rarer commodity. On the other his caste specialization was deepened, because over a period of several generations a slave family tended to become expert in a particular branch of work, but also to be thoroughly cut off from other kinds of activity. In the time of Diocletian a personal and hereditary hierarchy of situations and professions was established by law. This peak of specialization included freemen, freedmen, and slaves in one common service group. The universal reduction of personal freedom and individuality which such a move entailed tended to blur the distinction between the slave and the freeman, and to reduce both to the condition of serfs in the service of the state.

Serfdom of this sort represents an advanced and rigid stage of human social specialization. Another conspicuous example of it is offered by the ancient and, until very recently, the immutably rigid caste system of India. The Hindu institution of caste appears to have taken its origin in military conquest resulting in the mingling of victor and vanquished races. In the Laws of Manu, compiled soon after the beginning of the Christian era, strict rules are promulgated concerning marriage within and without caste, and four castes are recognized, with a fifth—an outcast group—reserved for the children of mixed-caste marriages. These castes early took on a decided vocational specialization. Thus the Brahmins were the spiritual counselors of people and state, the Kshatriyas were its warriors and administrators, the Vaisyas were burgesses, yeomen, and graziers, and the Sūdras were the servants of all the other castes. The cultural position of an infant, and hence his predestined occupation, were absolutely determined by his birth. There is probably no recent people in the world where the weight and force of the individual has been so subordinated to that of the body social as in the domain of India.

There can be no question that slavery has played an important part in human social evolution in many times and places. Yet despite this, the institution has never become sufficiently firmly established to leave really indelible marks on any living people, nor permanently to differentiate qualities of caste either in master or in slave. Yet some of its effects, even if transitory, can probably be detected. Some of them strike very close to home. For instance, an Englishman, Denis Brogan, has suggested that whereas the Virginia gentry of the eighteenth century produced Washington, Jefferson, Madison, Chief Justice Marshall, and other universal geniuses, Virginia after two generations of slaveholding produced only the great military men—Lee and Jackson and Johnston. To the degree that this observation is valid, the situation represented a great but a much more narrowly specialized contribution.

The evolution of parasitism, caste, and slavery among societies of mankind, it should be borne in mind, affects only the cultural field. It involves no immutable modifications of instinct or of physique, as it does among the social invertebrates. There, social parasitism and the institution of slavery have much more closely approached their logical termination. Both situations are of intense interest, and comparison between these invertebrate biological and human cultural phenomena may be illuminating. But it is always to be emphatically remembered that since this analogy is not direct, such a comparison may also be most deceptive. The broader and truer significance of these phenomena lies in the way they illumine one great factor of earthly evolution which affects all animals and men, individuals and societies alike. This is the reversal of the trend to complexity which may occur in response to certain environmental conditions common to societies the world over.

CHAPTER 7

Organic Evolution

THREE GREAT parameters of social evolution have been stressed in this book. The first is a trend toward the increasing complexity of societies with the passage of evolutionary time. This parameter is well-nigh universal, generally affecting not only societies as the term is usually understood, but the evolution of all life, and quite possibly, within the solar system, the evolution of matter as well. The second is more limited. It involves a concurrent trend toward the more efficient integration of social structures. While it is very widely reflected among the societies of the earth, it is not universal, for certain types of social organizations seem unaffected by it, and the behavior of the societies of man conforms to it only in part. The third parameter is a tendency, under certain special conditions and at certain social levels, toward a reversal of the trend to complexity leading back along the road of modification or loss of role and function to greater over-all simplicity and sharper specialization. Many special situations of intense interest fall within this last category.

What common ground do these great parameters of evolution have? What links them in their operation? What underlying causes bring them about?

In so far as societies and life itself are involved in these questions, the answers must lie in the mechanisms of organic evolution —in the genesis and the competitive survival of life and of the societies built from living things. These answers are not completely known in all their complexity. Yet the main outlines are clear. Rooted in the Darwinian concept of evolution, they take their flower in the tremendous elaboration and modification of that theory which mark its contemporary growth. The three parameters, in short, must be linked through certain aspects of neo-Darwinian evolutionary theory, and of modern population genetics.

When Darwin wrote the *Origin of Species,* he was largely unaware of what have come to be some of the most fundamental considerations underlying modern theories of evolution and natural selection. In the truest sense of the word he was a prophet. It is a profound tribute to his towering genius that the ideas which he outlined and developed throughout his life seem more correct and more universal when viewed in the light of later knowledge than they did in his own time. For he evolved a profoundly important theory with no knowledge of two of its very foundation stones. These are the fact that the units of heredity are particulate in nature, and the fact that the substance of heredity can undergo sudden changes of constitution and of function which may ultimately profoundly alter the nature of a species. If he had known these things, Darwin might well have perceived and outlined certain implications of his theory which are clearer to us today. Some of these implications are of particular pertinence to the mechanisms of the evolution of societies.

In writing the *Origin of Species* Darwin let stand a long-held assumption that in inheritance the characteristics of the parents are transmitted in a mingled and diluted form. This was the common belief of his time. It is as though red and blue streams from two vessels had been commingled to give a purple fluid which, while it might be tinted to green or yellow by admixture with a green or yellow liquid in the next generation, could never again be resolved into its original components. This belief had been held for centuries, and few had challenged it. Yet in its very simplest consequences it ran counter to observed facts of nature. For if every generation represents a uniform mingling of the traits of its ancestors, the variability of each generation of sexually reproducing organisms must, as the race moves on, be successively reduced. Such an assumption accounts all too well for the trend to simplicity. But on this basis it is difficult to understand anything of the vaster and more significant trend to complexity, or, indeed, to comprehend how the radiating processes of organic evolution occurred at all.

There was one who had worked before Darwin wrote the *Origin of Species* and whose results were published shortly afterwards, who did not share this common belief that inheritance was of a blending nature. He believed instead that individual hereditary characteristics were transmitted in a discrete manner—that is to say, they were transmitted as independent and indivisible units. Gregor Johann Mendel was born of peasant parents in Austrian Silesia in 1822 and entered the Königinkloster in Brünn in 1843. Ordained as a priest in 1847, he had a strong bent for natural science, and studied in that field in Vienna from 1851 to 1853. At the close of his formal studies he returned to Brünn and entered the profession of teaching, as an instructor in the physical and natural sciences. But Mendel was more than a teacher. He was an experimentalist *par excellence*. It was not long before he was deep in an investigation which was to become of revolutionary importance.

Mendel set to work simply to repeat the breeding experiments reported by earlier pioneers in the field of plant genetics —by Kölreuter, Knight, and Goss, and their colleagues. As his first experimental material of importance he used various races of the garden pea. Two features made his experiments of unusual significance. The first was his own rather extensive training in the exact sciences. This prompted him throughout his work to seek for data which could be simply expressed in quantitative terms. Whereas the earlier plant breeders had dealt with large complexes of genetic qualities in their experiments, Mendel constantly sought to work with the simplest possible characteristics of his plants that he could record—roughness or smoothness of seed coat, green or yellow coloration of the seeds, tallness or shortness of plant growth, and so on.

The second factor of importance to the work was perhaps accidental, or perhaps the unconscious product of genius. As the young Pasteur appears in the light of history either to have had uncanny fortune, or to have been immensely skillful in his choice of tartaric acid as one of the few chemical compounds then known in which he could have demonstrated the phenomenon of chemical isomerism through its effect on crystal structure, so in selecting the garden pea for his work, Mendel was remarkably fortunate in picking one of the plant materials best calculated to illustrate the thesis that the causative agents in heredity are of particulate character. Like many before him, he observed that the hybrid offspring of two different races of plants were in general intermediate in characteristics between their parents. But among his peas he also noticed that this condition resulted, not from a general blending of qualities, but rather from the fact that certain characteristics of each parent disappeared in the hybrid, to be more or less completely overlaid by the corresponding characteristics of the other. He made the further observation that when members of the hybrid generation were crossed, all of the qualities which had disappeared in the initial cross reappeared in the following generation in undiminished intensity. Moreover, it was found that the statistical distribution of these traits among the progeny in the third generation could best be accounted for by assuming that they were caused by separate entities within the germ plasm. In inheritance these were assorted independently and were either expressed or suppressed in combination with their partner units or *genes.* Those which were expressed were called *dominants;* those which were suppressed became known as *recessives.*

To speak today of the genes—the "atoms" of heredity—as separate quantities which can assort independently in inheritance is to utter a commonplace. So one is apt to forget the grandeur and the essential novelty of the concept as it was elaborated by Mendel. Its implications for the theory of evolution and for the understanding of social evolution in particular are tremendous. If, as the older workers thought, inheritance is blending, then the inherent variability of any line of organisms must decrease in each generation. Thus, in the ordinary course of events, a species would be bound in a very short time to become monotonously uniform. The only alternative to this would be that sudden, radical changes in the genes would take place at a high enough rate to maintain and increase the variability of the species over and beyond the monotonous smoothing effect of heredity. For this to happen would require a far higher rate of change or *mutation* in the genes than is found experimentally. But if, on the other hand, the genes are moderately discrete entities, which can be rearranged in inheritance, and further, if it is possible for recessive genes to exist in the germ plasm of a species for long periods with little or no bodily expression, then a store of hidden variability, as it were, can be built up in that species. This store can be carried on undiminished in a race, and may be as rich as the possible permutations and combinations of the genes themselves.

The complexity of this chain of reasoning may well have obscured its importance. Mendel's pioneer paper, contributed to the little-read publication of the Society of Naturalists of Brünn, gathered dust unheeded for thirty years while the Age of Darwin came and went. It was finally resurrected and given its proper place of significance by a man who was also to call attention for the first time to the second great factor in organic and social evolution—that of mutation.

In 1900 Hugo de Vries of Amsterdam, with co-workers in Germany and Austria, undertook to repeat the work of Mendel. They soon extended his earlier conclusions. As time went on, De Vries concentrated his breeding efforts upon a group of beautiful yellow-flowered plants—the evening primroses of the genus *Oenothera*. Now this choice was quite as fortunate as was that of the garden pea by Mendel. For if the garden pea was unusually well adapted to demonstrate the unitary character of many hereditary factors, the evening primrose was particularly suited to illustrate another phenomenon which up to that time had not been given proper significance, or even, perhaps, noticed at all.

This was the phenomenon of *saltation*. By this is meant a sudden, discontinuous shift in the hereditary characteristics of a line of organisms which, once it has occurred, may persist in the new form indefinitely and be as faithfully transmitted in heredity as any other characteristic of a line. It is probable that what De Vries first observed in his unexpectedly varying lines of evening primroses was not what modern geneticists would call true mutations, but involved gross changes of the chromosomes rather than of the genes themselves. So far as its external expression was concerned, however, the phenomenon was much the same. With abundant clarity De Vries proved that breeding lines of organisms may reproduce true to type for countless generations, and that then, suddenly, variations may appear which thereafter will be faithfully transmitted. Thus a single species, through the accumulation of many small changes, may gradually alter in character.

Thus there had been discovered three elements an understanding of which is requisite to an analysis of the processes of evolution. The first is Darwin's idea of natural selection. Second is Mendel's theory of the unitary inheritance of characteristics which can assort in a statistically predictable way from generation to generation and some of which will be wholly or partially recessive to others in inheritance. Finally, there is De Vries' conception that sudden changes may occur in characteristics which have remained stable for generations and that these characteristics, once changed, may continue to be inherited thereafter in their altered form. They are associated with abrupt changes in the structure of the chromosomes or in that of the genes themselves. These latter changes are mutations in the modern sense. With these three concepts in mind, it is not difficult to grasp the main outlines of the evolutionary process, and to make a beginning in applying it to the evolution of societies.

At the outset it is necessary to call attention to some factors with respect to the action of genes which were unknown to early geneticists. Thus, although it is now considered probable that many genes are more or less discrete entities, perhaps of molecular size, and are located in the chromosomes, it is equally clear that their action is by no means so atomistic in character as Mendel supposed. Genes are by no means always independent of one another. Frequently they are profoundly affected by their neighbors. This can be shown by experiment when the chromosomes in which they lie have been broken and are realigned. Although it is probable in many cases that such processes have little effect on the genes as such, old genes with new neighbors may produce very different effects. Furthermore, the genes are far from unitary in their action on the external bodily features of the organisms which they inhabit. Many genes can—indeed they often do—co-operate in inducing a single bodily feature of an animal or plant, and the action which each of them can exert is profoundly influenced by the other co-operating members. Thus tailless strains of mice, for instance, may carry many genes for specific tail characteristics, but under the circumstances they can find no means of bodily expression.

Not only can many genes co-operate to influence a single feature of an organism, but there are probably few single genes which affect only a single bodily feature of the plant or animal which they inhabit. The recessive gene for white eyes in the fruit fly is regarded as being as nearly a unitary character as can be imagined, for in inheritance it assorts in the simplest of all Mendelian ratios. Yet it also brings about quite other bodily changes, apparently unrelated, in certain portions of the abdomen of the males. These changes are nonetheless associated with the production of the white eye. The very mechanism by which genes produce their visible effects, as it is partially understood today, is such that it would rarely be expected that a single gene would account for one and only one effect in the organism which it modifies.

Finally, it is important to remember that the genes do not—as Mendel imagined from his first experiments—assort completely independently in inheritance, but that they are associated into linkage groups. These correspond physically to the chromosomes.

These linked genes are inherited together, though each group as a whole assorts independently of other groups. This means that genetic characteristics which are disadvantageous or are of neutral value to the organism may be firmly linked to other characteristics which are of predominant survival value. Thus, shielded by them in evolution, as it were, they may persist for very long periods merely by virtue of the fact that, under normal circumstances, they are inseparable from the benefactor genes and the damage which they cause the organism is much less serious than the evolutionary advantages conferred by their partners.

These apparently trivial details might be thought to have very little modifying influence on the grand pattern produced by the interaction of gene inheritance, gene mutation, and natural selection in evolution. However, it is important to notice them carefully. For it must always be borne in mind that it is primarily the *physical characteristics* of the organism, external and internal, rather than the gene content as such, which are subjected to the pressures of evolution. The organism or the society must first of all be efficient enough to hold its own against others that are in direct competition with it. How this efficiency is genetically achieved is of secondary importance to evolution. Under such circumstances apparently minor variations upon the major genetic theme may bring about results of far-ranging significance which are not fully explicable unless proper account is taken of them. A pertinent example of this may be the very phenomenon of the birth of societies in evolution.

Relatively little is known of the natural causes of mutations, though it is clear that they may be brought about experimentally by ionizing radiations and it has lately been demonstrated that they can be produced by certain chemicals. But it is evident beyond doubt that mutations in general occur fortuitously, and their physical expression in the organism is, for all practical purposes, at random. So far as is known, individual mutations, whether adaptive or unadaptive in nature, do not occur predominantly in any particular direction, though their expression may be conditioned by the action of other mutations which have preceded them. Apparently, individual gene mutations *per se* merely contribute to the inherent variability of the species in which they occur.

This inherent variability is one of the basic raw materials of evolution. It is not an element which can be detected by mere inspection. For within any continuous interbreeding population—and this is what the geneticists often mean by a species—the variability may be made up largely of mutated but recessive genes, carried in the germ plasm from generation to generation. Normally these are but rarely expressed, and even then very partially so, in that small changing fringe of the population which is by chance homozygous for one or another of the abnormal characteristics—that is, which carries the mutated gene in both members of a chromosome pair. Yet this variability is nevertheless always present in latent form—a stored bank account of genes—ready to be drawn upon when the environment changes suddenly or when, through severe competition or some other cataclysm, the species is obliged to move into novel and unaccustomed surroundings. Thus it is one of the most important of all factors in evolution.

If mutation and evolution were synonymous, the trend to complexity would be a formidable movement indeed, but there would be even more randomness, and far less of organization, in life and in the structure of societies. But actually in the reaction of the mutating organism with its environment there are certain important restraining forces which condition and direct its evolutionary course in such a fashion that its final adjustment is by no means fortuitous.

What are the restraining effects upon the explosive and random mutational tendencies inherent in all of life? Natural selection is the most obvious retarding force. Indeed, it appears no less impressive and potent a factor today than it did when Darwin first elucidated it. Any mutation which is expressed in the physical constitution of a plant or animal and is to persist in evolution must render the organism which bears it better able to triumph in the fierce competition of life, or it must be genetically linked to one which does so. This may be effected by better fitting the plant or animal for survival in the natural situation in which it already successfully dwells. It can also be achieved by permitting the mutated organism to escape from the pressure of the competition of its own species by invading and adjusting to new environs.

Now the number of chance mutations which will contribute to this result in any given situation represents an extremely small proportion of those which have occurred in the life of the species. Accordingly they will be highly selected, even initially. Further, the more completely an organism is adjusted to its environment, the rarer will be the random gene mutations which will further perfect its situation, and the more severe the selection will be.

Therefore highly adapted and modified organisms, exquisitely specialized to a particular environment, are, on the whole, more rigid, less easily modified, and more completely at the mercy of their surroundings than those more generalized types which are still imperfectly adjusted to any particular ecological niche, but are equipped to survive passably in several. The specialized and perfectly adjusted forms of life, being thus less flexible than more generalized ones, are notoriously more likely to become extinct with a sudden change of the environment. This may well be a contributory factor to the picture so often presented in evolution, in which whole groups of highly evolved and specialized organisms—armored fishes and giant amphibians, dinosaurs and saber-toothed tigers—have successively died out after periods of spectacular success, relinquishing their hard-won but changing kingdoms to less highly modified and more plastic competitors.

But the genetic state of the organism and the degree of its specialization are only two of the significant factors. The nature of the environment is also supremely important. Indeed, it is often so nearly a decisive factor as almost to define and limit the extent of the trend to complexity.

Imagine, for example, a biologically generalized organism invading for the first time the well-watered tropical or subtropical portions of the earth. It faces an extraordinarily intricate background against which it must evolve. For such environments provide many possible conditions of living and offer many possible means of livelihood. There may be trees amid which a comfortable arboreal existence can be supported or heavy rocks beneath which subterranean pygmies may find permanent shelter, or again streams which will support aquatic forms or open spaces in which flying types will be at home.

Now when this hypothetical pioneering species first enters such a complex realm it may be a homogeneous, interbreeding population. Generalized and comparatively versatile as its members are, they may enter several of the living spaces provided by this complex environment. If the area is fairly free of similar types and competition is therefore low, they may succeed in several of them. For a considerable period the species may continue as a versatile, uniform population, characterized by great flexibility but also by low particular skills in fully exploiting specialized situations.

This idyllic condition, however, will be of brief duration. For if competition in such an environment does not come from without the species, it will soon be provided from within. A population released amid such ideal surroundings can hardly fail to increase rapidly in numbers. It will not be long before competition for survival becomes so intense among the members of the species themselves that they are literally forced to specialize in order to increase their efficiency in living. Bit by bit—under the pressure of natural selection conditioned by the environment—some members of the original group may become specialized to an aquatic existence. Within that environment, and within that environment alone, they will eventually acquire sufficient skill to outwit their more generalized competitors and so to survive despite a diminishing food supply. At the same time, as their aquatic skills increase, their generalized skills will fall away. Less and less often will they attempt to invade the other environments they once knew so well. Finally they may abandon them altogether. While this aquatic group is adjusting to its new surroundings, other segments of the originally homogeneous species may have invaded and become specialized to an aerial environment, and still others to the environment of the treetops. Ultimately this species, once single and homogeneous, will be split into many groups so widely divergent as scarcely to be recognizable as of the same lineage. One aspect of the trend to complexity will have been achieved.

Many examples illustrate the various steps in this evolutionary process. Over and over again evidence can be found of an ancient generalized type of organism which, arising within or migrating into a complex environment, has radiated widely to fill the various special situations available to it, as the increasing pressure of its numbers forced an ever-growing specialization. For instance, until comparatively recent geologic times placental mammals never penetrated in any numbers into the ancient land-masses represented by present-day Australia and the adjacent islands. Only the archaic marsupials—animals such as opossums and kangaroos —and the yet more primitive monotremes—egg-laying mammals —were present to represent the stocks of warm-blooded, furred creatures.

Today the monotremes have all but disappeared. Yet a hint of the degree to which they must have become diversified in evolution remains in the extraordinary gulf in form and habits which exists between the only two representatives left on earth. On the one hand there is the spiny anteater, with its love of the uplands, its strong powers of digging, and its rapacious appetite for the social insects, and on the other the duck-billed platypus, with its soft fur and aquatic habits, its burrows in the riverbanks, and its diet of earthworms and slugs.

Among the marsupials, more links in the story remain to illustrate most vividly the evolutionary tendency of a single group of living things to diversify amid a complex environment. Thus in Australia alone they have exhibited the most spectacular radiation in evolution. This parallels many similar developments of the placental mammals in like environments elsewhere in the world.

Arising from a primitive generalized stock distantly akin to our Virginia opossum, there have developed on the Australian continent marsupials superficially resembling mice, rats, and squirrels —the last including gliding forms, functionally akin to our flying squirrel—moles, badgers, bears, and even wolves, to say nothing of the great range of variation and adaptation represented by the various wallabies and kangaroos, which find no close parallel among the higher mammals.

One of the finest examples of this sort of evolutionary radiation is that of the finches of the Galápagos Islands—of the genera *Geospiza, Certhidea, Pinaroloxias,* and *Camarynchus.* It is of particular interest because it has occurred relatively recently, and on a sufficiently restricted scale for its various steps to be still evident. When, in the course of its famous voyage, the *Beagle* stopped at the Galápagos Islands, Darwin took particular note of these rather sluggish and inconspicuous finches. In spite of their dun colors, their poor powers of flight, and their unmusical songs, other features about them attracted him greatly. Since the time of the great naturalist these birds—which have come to be popularly known as Darwin's finches—have been the subject of very careful study by evolutionists, and this study has revealed some extraordinary things.

All of Darwin's finches exhibit fundamental points of resemblance. Their nesting and courting habits are basically alike, as is their manner of rearing the nestlings. The eggs, too, are similar in shape, in color, and in markings among all the species. In various of their more detailed anatomical features, all of them are obviously related. Yet they exhibit an extraordinary diversity of habit among the four genera and the fourteen or more species into which they are now classified.

Some of them are relatively large birds, resembling black Java sparrows. These spend much time on the ground and feed largely on seeds, being equipped with heavy and powerful beaks. Others are primarily tree-haunting and bud-feeding in nature, with hooked bills vaguely suggestive of parrot beaks. Still others are insectivorous, and so like the warblers in habit that they were long mistaken for such birds, and their affinities to the finches have only recently been recognized. Finally and most remarkable of all, a single species has evolved into a woodpecker type. With its stout, straight bill, it chisels the treetrunks, and then exhibits the most astonishing modification of all. True woodpeckers, in addition to their sharp chiseling beaks, are equipped for their trade with an extensile, brush-tipped tongue. With this the cavity of the wood may be probed once it has been laid bare. The woodpecker finch, while lacking this structural adaptation, has made up for it by a remarkable habit. Plucking a cactus spine and holding it in the beak endwise with the sharp point projected forward, the wood-pecker finch industriously probes the cavity which it has made. As soon as any insect life appears, it drops the spine and with alacrity seizes its prey.

Careful and extensive studies of Darwin's finches leave little doubt that the present series of variously adapted birds represents the end result of the radial evolution of a single species. In remote times this species may have arrived in the Galápagos Islands from the adjacent South American mainland. It seems probable that the first-comers were more or less typical seed-eating finches. Such a form is still approximately represented in the Galápagos by certain members of the existing series. There is collateral evidence that the Galápagos finches arrived earlier than any other bird at present living in the islands, and it seems probable that for many generations they had the land to themselves. Under such conditions, the descendants of the first migrants probably increased rapidly until they approached the limit of population which could be supported by the existing resources. Then it was, presumably, that the pressure to exploit other opportunities of the environment—to shift from a diet of seeds to one of insects, to shift from the typical ground- and shrub-dwelling habits of the normal finches to the habitat of the tree-living groups, even to shift to the wood-drilling habits of the woodpecker—became especially severe, and evolutionary radiation took place in response to it.

This in miniature is the typical interaction of a complex environment and the life which inhabits it. By virtue of the ability of living things to mutate in a random fashion and to store those mutations in recessive form to make up the hidden variability of a species, there is inherent in life a perpetual tendency to radiate in evolution, unless that tendency is radically suppressed and controlled. Diversification such as this is basically a reflection of the diversity and complexity of the inanimate environment amid which life must exist and to which it must constantly adapt itself. It is as though the earth were a template or mold against which life was more and more closely pressed as it increased in abundance, until every wrinkle, every irregularity, every least detail of indentation of the mold had been reproduced.

Nor is this all. For it is to be emphasized once again that life itself is an important part of the environment of life. Thus as living matter increases in complexity, the very environment to which subsequent generations must adjust becomes proportionally more intricate. The result may be an accelerating progression of the trend to complexity. The evolution of the modern horse could never have occurred unless the higher grasses had first populated the plains. Again, all the arboreal adaptations of tree-living birds, mammals, and insects must perforce have waited on the appearance of trees themselves.

To a greater extent than is often realized, the world presents the complex system that it does largely because of the forms of life which have moved across it in ages past. Examples of the complicating effect of life on its own complexity might be greatly multiplied. They reach a climax in the interaction of a social individual with that most complex of all organic environments—its own society.

This reciprocal interaction of complex environments and natural selection, while a most potent factor in the trend to complexity, is not the only causative mechanism involved. There are others. Their consideration requires some discussion of the nature of a genetic species and of the bank account of variability which it possesses. It has already been emphasized that, in a genetic sense, a species is a relatively homogeneous population, all members of which are potentially able to breed with all other members. Thus there is theoretically no block to the free flow of genes within the length and the breadth of such a population. Now if this population unit is large, its potential variability in the form of the recessive mutant genes and gene complexes which it carries will be distributed among its members in a manner which, while it cannot be predicted for the individual, may be adequately expressed for the whole in a statistical fashion.

Take an idealized example of this situation. Assume the unit to be a large, homogeneous population of the fruit fly *Drosophila melanogaster*. From time to time in the history of the group, a recessive mutation for white eyes occurs at a characteristic rate, which is gradually propagated through the mass as the individuals carrying it breed. Another recessive mutation, which brings about a failure of wing development, also occurs with characteristic frequency and is similarly spread. Still a third mutation, producing abnormally large size and a dark body coloration, likewise takes place at a definite average rate. It too is recessive and is disseminated rather generally through the population.

Now under the normal conditions amid which *Drosophila* lives, if the mutation for wing loss were physically expressed, it would presumably be fatal in a very large number of instances. The mutation for white eyes, if expressed, might be mildly disadvantageous, particularly if it were associated with other enfeebling characteristics, but it would probably not be fatal. The mutation involving unusual bodily size and vigor and dark coloration might be actually advantageous under similar circumstances. Yet so long as the population remained large, well-adjusted, homogeneous, and freely interbreeding, an equilibrium would obtain between the rate of occurrence of these mutations and the rate of their elimination from the population (or increase within it) by natural selection. Thus the frequency of such mutated genes would tend to remain at a characteristic level in the population from generation to generation. The statistical chance would be small of the damaging mutations being eliminated or of the favorable mutation increasing predominantly within the species.

In the overwhelming majority of cases, these new mutations would exist only in the heterozygous form, where they would not physically appear and could exert no immediate evolutionary effect. Nevertheless, these heterozygous individuals would constitute a hidden "storehouse" of such mutated genes, for better or for worse. Unless the conditions of the environment suddenly changed, so as to radically favor some mutant, a breeding population such as this might remain stable for a very long time. Indeed, if the environment were absolutely stable, and the population completely in equilibrium with it, it might not evolve at all, despite the fact that the rate of random mutation within the species might actually be high.

This model is a realistic one, for in nature large and well-adjusted populations of organisms of this general type do in fact tend to evolve extremely slowly. Sometimes, as in certain marine mollusks, it is almost impossible to detect any change. There are living forms which have changed so little after nearly four hundred million years of existence that they can hardly be distinguished from their fossils. Furthermore, the guess that a rapid mutation rate will not necessarily secure a high rate of evolution in a large interbreeding population is evidently also correct, for in the fruit fly *Drosophila*, the mutation rate of which is high, evolution has apparently been comparatively slow.

It is probably safe to make the general statement that in large, dominant, and well-adjusted breeding populations evolution must be slow, even though mutation rates may be high. But it likewise follows that these slowly evolving large populations will accumulate a tremendous evolutionary credit, so to speak, in the genetic bank of their variability. For if it is true that in such populations individuals that are able to express any considerable number of recessive mutations rarely become abundant, it is equally true that an immense number of divergent recessive and hidden—and thus protected—mutations will accumulate in the germ plasm in the heterozygous condition. This credit will be at once an asset and a liability. For some of these hidden mutations would be lethal if expressed, and others would be highly disadvantageous. Yet others might be indifferent, while a few would almost certainly improve the performance of the organism, either in its current environment or amid new conditions which might arise.

So much for the stable population in a stable environment. Consider, now, the consequence of some unusual environmental condition operating upon this idealized fruit-fly population. Suppose that in the course of ever-increasing distribution and in the hungry search for new territory small sectors of the population are carried by winds over high and inhospitable mountain ranges into various fertile but mutually isolated valleys. What will be the course of evolution thenceforward of all these small and fragmented colonies now cut off from the main body and isolated from each other as well?

To take the simplest case first, suppose that the various new environments in which the fragments of the population have now been isolated are strictly identical in character. It might seem that in such case the isolated sub-populations would continue to evolve in a strictly parallel manner. Reflection shows, however, that the mere act of isolating these fragments will contribute to their diversification, quite apart from the effect of the new environment. It is here that the accumulation of hidden genes comes into play. For in a small population fragment, the proportion of hidden gene mutations to the total gene content of the group will almost certainly be considerably shifted from what it was in the original sample. Some of the mutated genes may be lost altogether. Others may be much commoner than they were, relatively speaking. For these the chances are no longer small that two individuals heterozygous for the recessive genes will mate and so give rise to a proportion of progeny which are pure for them and thus able to express them. In fact, they may be very large. So almost immediately there will be a tendency to draw on this part of the "bank account" and to convert the long-hidden gene stock of the original population into tangible cash.

But the endowment of the variability which the fragments of the original population have inherited will of course not be identical, and this will soon become apparent. Thus one portion of the hypothetical population might contain the genes for white eye in relatively high proportion, but totally lack those for winglessness and for robustness. Another might contain winglessness and robustness only, while a third might possess solely the wingless gene.

In the large population these differences might have remained concealed, so long as the total percentage of individuals carrying these mutations remained low. Now they become of immediate significance in evolution, for the old equilibrium between the number of mutant individuals which appear in each generation and the number of those that are adversely or favorably selected has been upset. The lethal recessives will tend to be selected out and eliminated, through the death of their homozygotes. The slightly disadvantageous ones may be tolerated if they are linked to others with more than compensating advantages. The few advantageous genes will be realized at last and there will be a strong tendency for them to increase in the population. Each of these small populations which showed such evolutionary stability while they were members of a large breeding whole may now begin to evolve rapidly. Within a few generations, several distinct races of fruit flies may have appeared in the isolated valleys, even though the living conditions in those valleys are strictly identical. In time these various races may become so far differentiated that they are no longer capable of breeding among themselves. Then, even if the geographic barriers are removed, they will have become permanently isolated. Henceforth they must be reckoned as different species.

There is abundant evidence that this process is going forward continually in nature. In fact, it is believed to be one of the important mechanisms through which new species are created. To be sure, the situation is never so simple as in our idealized examples, for the environments of various isolated valleys are rarely identical, as they have here been assumed to be. If the environments differ, of course, the adjustment between the organism and its environment emphasizes the gaps between the fragments of the population. They widen yet more strikingly, as each isolated population through natural selection tends to adjust itself as perfectly as possible to its own particular surroundings.

Thus the multiplicity of environments of the earth forms a major factor in the trend to complexity. But it is by no means the only one. The very mechanics inherent in the hereditary mechanism of living things reinforces that trend under certain conditions, even when the environment remains unchanged.

The whole mechanism of sexuality represents a powerful force in the trend to complexity. In every new generation of sexually reproducing organisms there must of necessity be an intimate mixing of differing gene complexes involving essentially half the total genetic potentialities of each of two individuals of a population. By its very nature this mixture tends to increase the variety of gene endowment of the individual and promote a wide dissemination of all the variable genetic elements throughout the breeding population. While the immediate expression of this variability is often held in check, the tendency to complexity inherent in the process is a very powerful one, ready at any time to escape should the various controls which keep it in bondage slacken.

How vital the mechanism of sexual cross-fertilization is to the welfare and even the survival of higher groups of organisms is indicated by the unusual devices which preserve it in many species where without such devices cross-breeding would be difficult. For example, among the ants and the termites we have the great dispersion flights of the males and perfect females at breeding time. This unexpected process is wholly inconsistent with the sedentary, subterranean lives which these creatures normally lead. Yet it is highly effective in ensuring that an exchange of genes shall take place between widely separated communities and so, evidently, has been emphasized in evolution. Again, among the higher, insect-pollinated plants, the intricacy and beauty of flower development which so enriches the natural world contributes to this same end. Even in man the tendency is sometimes evident, as in the elaborate systems of custom, tradition, and taboo which have been built up in certain primitive exogamous groups to ensure that close inter-marriages in families will be prevented. In man, however, the social situation is much more complex, and many societies have existed and continue to exist in which close intermarriage is the rule, though marriages between full brothers and sisters are commonly frowned upon.

Yet another mechanism of complexity is inherent in the prin-ciples of heredity discovered by Mendel. This may be illustrated again by the hypothetical model of the fruit-fly population. Sup-pose that, as in the preceding case, the originally large breeding population has become separated into a number of very small frag-ments occupying isolated valleys which, as before, offer absolutely identical environments. The situation may be idealized further by assuming that—contrary to the more realistic postulate made in the last case—the distribution of the hidden genetic variability in the original population was retained absolutely uniformly in the isolated fragments. Thus, at the moment of its isolation, each re-tained fragment is not only identical with every other one in re-spect to all of its expressed genetic characters, and in respect to the environment, but it is further identical in respect to all hidden recessive gene mutations. In a word, the various fragments of the population are carbon copies of one another.

Even under these rigidly simplified and highly improbable conditions, the trend to complexity will assert itself. The popula-tion fragments will not long remain identical. It must be assumed that mutation will proceed as actively in the population fragments as it did before they became separated. Now, so long as these iso-lated fragments exceed a certain critical size, the evolution of the groups will be primarily Darwinian in nature, and selective to the environment. So long as this critical population size is maintained, the environment will be a predominant factor in evolution. Thus, on this special assumption, the various groups should continue to evolve in parallel fashion.

However, if a group happens to fall below this minimum number of individuals, a very strange situation is presented. In so small a population any mutation which happens to occur with relatively high frequency may succeed in establishing itself and will have a reasonable probability of actually dominating the genetic constitution of the population quite irrespective of whether it is helpful or harmful, so long as it is not positively lethal in its action. In this case, at last, the evolution of the organism has become entirely divorced from its environment. Under these peculiar circumstances, mutation becomes evolution, and evolution, like mutation, then becomes essentially random in its nature. Only one controlling factor—that of population size—has been removed. Every other controlling factor has been rigidly maintained. And still the trend to variability and diversity persists.

One more consequence of these mechanisms of the evolution of populations should be considered. Once more, take the model *Drosophila* population and suppose that it is existing as a large and continuous species unit, evolving very slowly to keep pace with its slowly changing environment. Suddenly a natural cataclysm occurs, too great for the species as a whole to meet from its immediate genetic resources of adaptability. What will happen?

When the disaster strikes, a fragmentation of the population will probably occur. Let us further suppose, then, that the species is broken up into many small and genetically non-homogeneous units, inheriting different proportions of the many-faceted store of hidden variability inherent in the larger population. Such of these fragments as are below the critical size where adaptive evolution may take place will probably perish quickly. Random evolution is hardly likely to succeed amid these new and demanding conditions. But for those population fragments which are still in the range where adaptive evolution can take place, a severe challenge and also a great potential opportunity are presented. It is precisely in such groups that effective adaptive evolution can take place most rapidly.

Thus there may be one or even a few of these frail and tiny population communities that will succeed in avoiding extinction and in adjusting themselves to the profoundly new situation. Once they have come into fairly good equilibrium with the new environmental conditions, their fortunes will begin to rise. Eventually a new and radically altered type of population will succeed in attaining to large numbers. It will replace the large populations of its archaic ancestors and will overrun and annihilate the rare transitional forms which gave it birth. These transitional forms may thus become the missing links of organic evolution.

There are likewise many such rare or missing links in social evolution, as we have earlier seen, such as the Stenogastrine wasps or the primitive ancestors of man. Such annectent or linking forms are subjected to very severe competition both by the groups which give rise to them and by those better adjusted groups which follow them in evolution. It is not surprising that such transitional types are rare in the living world. Many paleontologists feel that the mechanism outlined above may be largely responsible for the scarcity in the fossil record of these immensely important innovators of the great evolutionary movements. For it follows very logically that small and evanescent groups of rare organisms, such as these rapidly evolving connecting series during the critical days of their development, would be precisely those least subject to preservation as fossils.

The broader implications of all these factors deserve final emphasis. Contrary to what one might think, the very large and dominant population—the conspicuous, abundant species—will, if it is in good equilibrium with its environment, tend in general to evolve slowly. However, it will also accumulate a large bank account of hidden variability, bad as well as good. This may lead to rapid evolution if the species should become fragmented and remain so for a comparatively long period. At the other extreme, in the exceedingly small population evolution may well occur extremely rapidly, but it will tend to be random and basically unadaptive. In the slightly larger population just above the critical limiting size, evolution will also be rapid, but it will tend to be basically adaptive.

The optimum situation for rapid and effective evolution would then seem to be that of a number of small but contiguous breeding populations which enjoy a certain percentage of exchange among themselves of breeding individuals. Such genetic pools connected by trickling streams may enjoy the benefits of variation and rapid evolution which pertain to the small, isolated group and at the same time may in considerable measure reap the advantages of the much greater variability inherent in the large population. It has been calculated that the optimum size of such a group may vary between 250 and 250,000 individuals. The early communities of primitive man doubtless fell well within this range of population. Also they were probably connected by slow and minute trickles of genes achieved through intertribal marriages. Thus this best of all evolutionary situations may well have been the heritage of man.

⫸ CHAPTER 8 ⫷

Social Evolution

THE THREE great parameters of evolution—complexity, integration, and specialization—obtain for societies no less than they do for populations of non-social living things. The basic mechanisms are the same, for the underlying demands of the earthly environment are essentially alike for social and non-social creatures. But a society represents yet another order of complexity in organization. It constitutes another step in the great panorama of evolution, and the most fascinating one, both by virtue of its intricacy and, most significantly, because it predominantly concerns man as a social being.

How did societies originate in the first place, and how did they hold their own in the early stages of their development? This is one of the most fascinating and baffling of all the problems of social evolution. It is posed by the case of the incipient community at every level of social existence. It is hard at first sight to believe, for instance, that the Stenogastrine wasp community in the Philippine Islands is a more effective entity than the well-integrated solitary wasp types from which it presumably arose. For on the one hand, communal ties are already so binding as to restrict the range and the activities of the colony members, while on the other specialization and co-ordination among members is not yet well enough developed for the colonial unit to function very effectively as a whole.

Some of the considerations of evolution suggested in the last chapter may offer a partial answer to this conundrum. Sometimes genes which are actually disadvantageous to a species are carried along from generation to generation and perpetuated in the germ plasm simply because they are indissolubly linked to an advantageous gene or set of genes. Eventually, through processes of intra-organismal adjustment, the disadvantageous characteristics may be converted into selectively helpful ones. It may well be that this process accounts for the early appearance and persistence of many innovations in nature.

This sort of explanation may well be applicable to the phenomenon of the origin of social life. It is not an unreasonable postulate that the tardy departure of the daughter Stenogastrine wasps from the maternal comb, the watchfulness and care of the primitive ant queen over her first brood, are characteristics which were linked in evolution to genes controlling other qualities of great survival value, such as high fecundity, long individual life, or unusual physiological plasticity and adaptability. This offers a plausible explanation of the rise and persistence of some of the first exceedingly inefficient societies, which certainly appears to have occurred in some cases well before those societies had acquired any obviously superior adaptive value by virtue of their constitution. Such an explanation, to be sure, is not wholly satisfying, and its purely gratuitous assumptions are beyond our capacities to test experimentally at present, although it is by no means impossible that experimental tests could be devised for them. It is at least a beginning—a point of departure into an unknown region which is otherwise uncharted.

Another factor in evolution may well be operative in the case of societies. In organic evolution the significant factor which influences the trend of a population is the newly adult and vigorously breeding individual. In the evolutionary scheme there is little room for the aged, for their elimination has a negligible influence on the genetic composition of the race. Thus generation after generation of aging wolves may perish of starvation or fall before the ravages of their younger kin without exerting the slightest influence on the total composition of the wolf population, for they have already bred within it. What is important for a population is that the individuals composing it shall pass through a vigorous and well-adapted breeding period. What happens to them after they have passed their prime is, in an evolutionary sense, of little consequence. Thus any characteristics which will promote an early and vigorous maturity, even if they lead to deformity in old age, will tend to be preserved in evolution.

Take the case of the Irish elk—a long-extinct race of deer with antlers which ultimately became so enormously developed that they may have been a positive impediment to the overburdened individual. How could this have happened? One possibility is this. The individual Irish elk which in old age was handicapped by its mighty antlers may also have been the youngster which developed its spike-horns well before the other bucks of its year, and so was able to battle for the young does more successfully than any of its youthful rivals. What matter if this same proud buck later became the stag with such overdeveloped antlers that it fell easy prey to the wolf? Long before that time it would have bred, passing both the desirable characteristic of early maturity and the undesirable one of later hypertrophy on down the stream of its race.

Apply this same reasoning to the primitive societies of insects. At maturity the incipient and fragile colony of the Stenogastrine wasp, like the elderly Irish elk, seems to have many characteristics to put it at a disadvantage beside its less evolved and in this case solitary competitors. But the situation is very different when this tiny family is being founded. In this context, let us consider the origin and the significance of the institution of the family as a whole in the evolution of living things.

If a species is to survive in the race of natural selection, each member must, on the average, be replaced in each generation by another individual, which must attain maturity and successfully breed. This means that every spawning salmon, every pair of robins, every mother bear must successfully rear two young to breeding maturity. On the face of it this is a simple requirement.

Actually, it is a most difficult one, in view of the intense hazards which face all wild creatures, particularly in the helpless days of their early immaturity.

There are two ways of meeting this difficulty. Both of them have been adopted countless times in organic evolution. The first is to produce such a tremendous number of offspring that, although they are protected very little during their most helpless period, the chances are almost overwhelming that an adequate number of them will escape all of the dangers confronting them and survive to maturity. This is the way of the fern, with its millions of little-developed spores, of the mussel with its myriads of eggs, of the salmon and the shad with their numerous spawn. It is the way of many parasitic organisms and societies—the tapeworm with its vast numbers of reproductive bodies and the parasitic ant with its swarms of little queens replacing the fewer and better-developed representatives of socially independent forms.

The other obvious device is not to depend upon absolute numbers, but to launch a relatively small number of offspring upon the world in a sufficiently advanced state so that their chances of survival will be much improved. Sometimes this end is effected physiologically. There is the viviparous fish carrying its living young relatively well-grown before they leave the shelter of the parent's body, the parasitic fly bearing its single mature larva ready to pupate as soon as it appears, the brush turkey or the Australian mallee fowl laying eggs so richly provisioned with yolk that when the chick hatches it is able to fly almost directly from the egg as a self-supporting young bird.

Sometimes this protection is achieved in yet another way—through especial parental care for the helpless young until they are sufficiently mature to fend for themselves with a reasonable chance of survival. This is the device through which the simplest form of society comes into being. For example, there is the male sunfish with its nest of eggs, the solitary wasp painstakingly pro-visioning its young with food, the mother bear bestowing nearly two full seasons of care upon her developing cubs, and the pair of robins with their well-tended fledglings. In this light, the family organization is a device to improve the survival chances of the young individual of a species at its most vulnerable period. That is the time which really counts in evolution. Judging from the widespread occurrence of the institution throughout living nature, the family—the simplest form of society—may have been of adaptive value from the very moment of its origin.

What is it that determines which course should be taken for survival in the evolution of any given species—the course of high fecundity with a low order of protection, or that of lower fecundity with higher protection? Some very interesting corollaries between the two situations may be significant. In any single evolutionary line of animals the members of the series which are more primitive in other ways frequently rely for survival upon high fecundity with a correspondingly low order of protection, while in the more highly evolved members of the group the reverse may be true. Thus the rather lowly organized mussel is highly prolific but gives no attention to the eggs once they are shed. By contrast the highly constituted solitary wasp lays relatively few eggs, but each is carefully and laboriously provided with a separate cell and abundant food. The primitive ostrich, and even the chicken and the duck, lay large clutches of eggs and start off with populous broods of young, a large share of which under natural conditions perish before reaching breeding maturity under the casual care which they receive, in contrast to the small broods and the exquisite parental care developed by most of the higher perching birds.

Why should this correlation between primitiveness and fecundity on the one hand and high organization and parental care on the other so often obtain? One reason may well be that natural selection for high fecundity in evolution is a comparatively direct and simple process which might have operated early in the evolutionary history of a line, resulting in highly fertile individuals that are relatively primitive. The development of the family, however, with its correlative necessities of highly elaborated instincts or intellect, and its development of complex behavior patterns on the part of parents and young alike, is far indeed from a direct or an elementary evolution. Such a change indubitably requires a relatively high degree of initial organization in the parents to make it possible. After it has been achieved the selectional pressure to high fecundity may be relaxed or actually inhibited.

Among solitary organisms very few cases are known in which the protection characteristic of the typical evanescent family is combined with the other survival device of extremely high fecundity. This is interesting and important. If it could be so combined, the organism achieving this double bid for survival might be in an unusually fortunate evolutionary position. Some attempts at this double bid for survival are familiar and spectacular, but they regularly fall short of success. Such may be the case, for instance, with the Chinese paradise fish, in which the extremely numerous small eggs are gathered into a bubble nest and carefully tended and pugnaciously defended by the male. In consequence, a large percentage hatch successfully into tiny lively young fish. At this point, however, the efficiency of family protection may break down badly, for a single adult can hardly keep adequate track of such a large, divergent, and active family, and they succumb in numbers to predators while they are still comparatively helpless. In similar case is the mother hunting-spider, her body completely covered with a swarm of tiny progeny to which she gives considerable protection for a time. But she abandons them while they are still young and comparatively helpless because it would be a physical impossibility for her to care for so many young when they were even half developed. It is doubtful if these two devices for survival have often been combined in evolution, for the important reason that one or two parents are necessarily sharply limited in the number of young that they can nurture with any degree of efficiency.

Two points have been made concerning the role of parental protection and of the evanescent family. First, the family may be regarded as a device that favors survival because it protects the young at a stage when they would otherwise be vulnerable and when they are of great significance as factors in the evolution of the species. At the same time, the very mechanics of the situation inherently inhibits a solitary species which adopts the family type of organization in evolution from remaining very fecund, for one or two parents can take adequate care of but a limited number of progeny. What bearing do these two factors have upon the mechanisms of the next step in evolution from the family toward the truly social state?

Suppose that among the members of an evanescent family of some incipiently social species certain mutations took place, leading on the one hand to prolonged longevity of the parent and, on the other, causing certain individuals of the progeny to remain at home when mature instead of wandering afield. Evidently these are the types of changes that actually occurred in the transition from solitary to social life among insects. The result would be a primitive social community. Awkward and ineffective in many ways, it would nevertheless be more efficient in one very important respect than the family from which it developed. For the first time it would provide an environment in which *both* roads to survival—protection *and* fecundity—might be simultaneously adopted.

For a group consisting of a mother and her breeding daughters, permanently associated and with their young gathered together, could adequately care for and protect a much larger number of progeny than could an equivalent number of solitary mothers, provided that all the parents shared in the protective activities of the community *all the time*. This is exactly the situation which frequently obtains among the most primitive of the social insects. It may well be that this opportunity of traveling on both of the roads to survival more than compensated for the serious disadvantages to which such evanescent societies would seem liable. The further progress and perfection of this evolution culminated in those huge insect communities in which both the care of the young and fecundity in reproduction are carried to such tremendous heights. In these the queens act as specialists in fecundity and the workers as experts in the protection of the young.

Another possible course of evolution of the primitive society is worth noticing. Suppose that in this semisociety composed of a mother and her essentially unmodified daughters a further change occurs. This time it is among the progeny, rendering them unfit in some physical or psychic manner to exist independently—decreasing their fertility or their stature, modifying their nesting instincts, or shortening their span of life—and thus bringing them into maladjustment with the existing environment. In the evanescent family form, in which the members must be able to care for themselves at maturity, such defective forms would quickly perish. In the true subsociety, however, in which the mother lives to give sanctuary to the young after they have reached maturity and in which a protecting home is already provided for them, these abnormal creatures may survive. Furthermore, since all of the young come from one or a few mothers, and are closely related among themselves, a change which affects one of them may be reflected in a considerable number. In such case the defective semisocial individual will find itself at a double advantage for survival compared to a solitary rival in like unfortunate case. Not only will it have a protected environment in which to hide and eke out its existence, but it will have much companionship in misery among its kinsmen which are as defective as itself. It is much less likely to be slaughtered like a defective young crow, or starved out by its hungry and dominating nest mates like the backward robin fledgling.

A brood in which all the members are defective in similar ways may command care from its parent, and—even more important—may provide mutual tolerance among its own members. It is not difficult now to imagine that once in many millions of times a series of mutations for defectiveness and dependence among the brood may have occurred which not only commanded increased devotion on the part of the parents and ensured mutual tolerance among the brood members, but which were actually helpful to the parents and of mutual benefit among the young themselves. Should this happen, we would have a situation somewhat like that among the bumblebees. There the defects of the little workers, their dwarfed stature, their permanent dependence upon the colony, and their exaggerated instincts to labor, are exactly of the kind to stabilize the existence of the community and to provide added protection to the developing brood of the parent female, including her own daughter queens, while at the same time binding them together more closely and rendering them more helpless as individuals. In the case of the social insects it is easy to imagine that this is the kind of development which actually occurred and, further, that these were the forces which propelled the evolving society over the difficult portion of its evolutionary road. Once such a society had appeared, it might acquire adaptive efficiency, permitting it to survive as a stable community.

This last development is the whole story of the trend to integration. It will be interesting to consider this trend first from the standpoint of the component of the society, and then from the standpoint of the society as a whole.

The close resemblance of the role of the individual in a society to that of the parasite has been described. Like the parasite, the social individual exists in a highly specific and critical environment, which demands the extreme perfection of certain capabilities and utterly neglects the development of many others, which latter ultimately tend to disappear. But the environment of the member of a society is even more critical and intricately demanding than that of a parasite. A host is usually a living environment of complex character which provides many ecological niches to be occupied by numerous types of specialized parasites. However, these parasites do not depend absolutely upon the continued life of the host for their survival in the sense that the members of a social organization depend upon the survival of that society. Accordingly, the parasite is under less exacting evolutionary conditions than is the social individual. The latter must not only survive in its specialized niche; it must so effectively collaborate with its fellows and its environment as to ensure the survival and the increasing efficiency of that environment as well. This is a condition as severe in its adaptive implications as the hottest, the driest, or the coldest area of the earth. At the same time it is infinitely more intricate. What wonder, then, that the members of a permanent society show such a marked trend to extreme adaptive specialization in both structure and function!

From the standpoint of the social structure as a whole, the problem of adaptation for survival is simpler and more straightforward. If the integrated social unit is to persist, it must extract a living from the earth with higher efficiency than its solitary competitors. Its members must be able to sustain and to rear to maturity on a given area of foraging ground greater numbers of fertile descendants, on the average, than would achieve maturity if all the parents were solitary individuals. In this way and in this way only can the mature adapted society successfully compete with its solitary kin for the raw materials essential to the maintenance of life and growth. Such an achievement requires that every component of the society be a specialist, more skilled in exploiting some niche of its environment than any related solitary organism can be. At the same time, it demands that more available aspects of the environmental niche be exploited by the social members in total than by their solitary competitors. It further demands that the combined results of the action of all these individuals be pooled in the generalized body of the social structure and utilized for the common benefit.

Cases are known in which some specialization of social individuals to the exploiting of particular portions of the total environment of the society has been demonstrated. For instance, the workers of a hive of honeybees develop individual specialties in flower-foraging, conditioned probably very largely by their initial experiences in the field. Thus one worker may become an expert for a day at least in finding and tapping blue flowers. Another will follow the techniques required to get honey from flowers with very deep throats, where nectar is difficult to secure. Thus a colony on any given day will probably obtain honey more efficiently from a terrain of varied flowers than an equal number of solitary bees would do. And through the device of the common comb and the exquisite mechanisms for internal co-ordination characteristic of the hive, this increased supply of nourishment becomes available to the entire community and is distributed among them in an unusually effective way.

If the nascent society is to survive and become adjusted to the world, it must fulfill a second requirement early in its evolutionary career. It must be able also to resist being driven from its foraging grounds by hungry and jealous rivals, social as well as solitary. Unlike its individual component, it must be able to maintain itself successfully in a varied, generalized environment. This requirement, like the preceding one, demands that the society become a well-integrated, smoothly functioning unitary structure. It demands that internal co-ordination become ever more perfect, that the social unit become increasingly like an individual in every aspect of its appearance and operation. Like the requirement of efficient food exploitation, this constitutes a powerful evolutionary drive to integration.

This requirement of successful self-defense has apparently led to another evolutionary trend. As societies evolve, it is their tendency to increase in absolute size and consequently in the inherent complexity of their internal constitution. Consider not only the simplicity but the minuteness of the primitive ant colonies as compared with the enormous societies of advanced species, of the little gatherings of the Stenogastrine wasps with the large colonies of the socially more advanced hornets.

Why this evolution to size, with its inevitable further increment of complexity? The full answer to this fascinating inquiry is not known. One answer may be that it represents the logical consequence of the simultaneous adoption of protection and fecundity as survival devices, with a concomitant retention of most of the young in the community. Another may be that under most circumstances, size itself confers an advantage on the social structure.

Provided the integrative evolution of the society has kept pace with its growth, it is not difficult to see how this might be true. If the society has actually achieved a higher efficiency per unit area than its solitary relatives in exploiting the foraging ground around it, then, other things being equal, the more ground that can be covered, the better off the society will be, and size will have an adaptive value in this sense. In addition, if the larger society is well-knit, a considerable advantage in competition for the best spaces of the earth and for the best of the available food supplies will accrue. Clearly, there are advantages to size in social evolution.

Inevitably, in considering the origin and growth of societies, the query arises—when did the social way cease to be merely a linked liability for the society itself and of real advantage only to the individuals composing it, and become well adapted in evolution from the viewpoint of the communal structure as a whole? Of all questions concerning the social way, this is one of the most fascinating, and it is one for which almost no data are at present available. It would be extremely valuable, for example, to know whether the individual members of a colony of Stenogastrine wasps act as specialists in their foraging, developing skills in the capture of distinctive types of prey, just as individual honeybees appear to do on given days in the exploitation of particular sorts of flowers. Next to nothing is known concerning these aspects of the fine structure of primitive societies. In the elucidation of how societies came to be there are few fields of inquiry which are in greater need of careful investigation.

One thing at least is certain. All the requirements for adaptive survival in a society, whether they relate to a more efficient exploitation of the environment or to more successful attack and defense, demand above all a specialization and simplification of the individual on the one hand, and on the other an increasingly efficient integration of the efforts of all of them. Viewed in this light, the trend to integration, with its severe sacrifice of the overall competence of the component individual, appears as the natural and inescapable result of the environmental forces amid which societies evolve and take their way.

Must the conclusion then be that this road to ever-increasing usurpation of the sphere of the individual by that of the society is the inexorable course of social development? The question is a grave one. For this is the philosophy of the unity and the supremacy of the society. Applied to the political aspect of the societies of men, it becomes the exact philosophy of totalitarianism.

Two kinds of society have been considered thus far—the *family* and the *integrated* form. The family consists of the evanescent and temporary association of one or two parents and their young. This association was probably formed because of the advantages which accrue in securing greater survival for the brood during its most vulnerable period. The typical family does not persist after the young are grown, although in some cases—the covey of quail or the pack of wolves—the grown young may remain together in a loose co-operative partnership for a period after they have attained maturity. So long as the typical family tends to disperse within the life span of the younger generation, it must remain a loosely integrated, generally co-operative structure, in which the individualities and spheres of action of its members are little reduced—and may, indeed, actually be increased. For if the life of the social organization is shorter than the effective breeding period of the individual, the individual cannot lose its competence to survive as an independent organism. Otherwise it will perish during the solitary portion of its life cycle, and the species will shortly disappear. Furthermore, so long as all the individuals of a family continue to breed at maturity, the forces of natural selection will continue to operate *between* them—*intracommunally*—just as they do between the members of a population of solitary individuals. The selective pressures on the family, therefore, would seem to be toward the retention of over-all competence on the part of the component individuals, and toward making the individual—not the society—the dominant and important element.

When, however, the family has developed into that more

specialized order of society represented in its primitive form by the Stenogastrine community and in its most highly evolved form by the huge colony of bee or termite, a most significant change has occurred. The society and the social environment have now become far more stable and enduring than the individual. This is the kind of social organization which I have called integrated in this book.

With the exception of the perfect sexual forms of many species, all the members of an integrated community of the social insects are born into the social milieu, live all their lives there, and die there. At no time in the whole life cycle are they called upon to face a solitary existence. Moreover, save in the case of the adult perfect females of such groups as the ants, which go through a brief solitary period in founding their colonies, the survival of the species does not depend upon the competence of its individuals as such. For most of them are non-breeding, and hence natural selection will not occur between them as individuals, but rather between whole communities—*intercommunally*—reflecting itself in the numbers and the success of the young fertile females produced by each social unit. For the integrated type of society and for this type of society alone, therefore, it would be expected that the trend of evolution would be toward the ultimate supremacy of the community over the individual. Further, the trend of evolution in this type of society has been toward the restriction of breeding individuals to a smaller and smaller fraction of the population in the community.

The evolutionary pressures on the family and on the integrated society, then, would seem in many respects opposite in character. Yet it seems clear that the one was derived from the other in evolution. Thus there must be characteristics inherent in the family which, under certain circumstances, can permit or encourage the trend to the integrated form of society. Some of these qualities are not far to seek.

It seems entirely reasonable to deduce that although the family will normally resist pressures toward integration and will remain a simple, generalized structure with a high order of individual independence among its members, nevertheless it contains potentialities which, under rather unusual circumstances which will later be discussed, may favor the explosive trend to specialization and interdependence characteristic of the integrated society. It must always be borne in mind that the family form is of vast importance in the social world. It has been developed innumerable times and exists in great abundance at all levels in nature. Integrated societies seem regularly to have been derived from those of the family type. Yet, in sharp contrast, examples of such integrated societies are very rare in nature compared with the widespread and abundant occurrence of the family form. This gives mute evidence of how rarely the integrated form has arisen or survived and further emphasizes its specialized character.

In assessing the inevitability of any trend to close integration in the social evolution of man, still another kind of social organization demands attention. It is of predominant significance, and it differs profoundly from the other two in many fundamental aspects. This society consists of a loose gathering of individuals coming together only after they are adult to form swarms or schools, flocks or herds. A school of minnows or of mackerel, a ball of hibernating snakes among the rocks of a mountaintop, a wheeling flock of pigeons, the migrating hordes of European lemmings, the great winter herds of barren-ground caribou, the vast waves of migrating fur seals of former years—all these and more are examples of societies of this kind. This type of aggregation represents what is ordinarily regarded as simple gregariousness. For purposes of convenience it may be termed the *associative* form of society.

This associative society is impermanent with respect to the individual, which normally exists as a solitary organism throughout a considerable portion of its life cycle. In this respect it is unlike the integrated but like the family form. Again like the family, the associative society consistently exhibits a low order of integration and a high order of independence and competence on the part of its members. Unlike the family, in its most typical expression it is formed of adult individuals and does not represent the milieu into which the individual is born. Unlike both of the others, the members of this gregarious group are not ordinarily closely related. The interactions between the associative society and the family and the integrated forms which co-exist in one social milieu have a fundamental bearing upon the problems of human civilization. It is on this associative side of communal living that mankind is wholly unique in the world. I know of no other animals living through a mixture of the family and associative social forms in which the associative type of social evolution can compare either in specialization or in dominance with the family pattern.

CHAPTER 9

The Ties that Bind

A MOST NOTABLE characteristic of the integrated social way of life is its astonishing stability. Integrated societies—particularly those of the higher orders—seem such fragile structures. It is a cause for wonder that they remain intact as long as they do, far outlasting the life spans of their members. Why is an ant colony so stable a structure when its members are exposed to all the vicissitudes that attend the lives of tiny earth-bound creatures—at the constant mercy of flood and drought, heat and cold, famine and the unremitting attacks of enemies? What gives this astonishing tenacity to a way of life apparently so vulnerable to destruction?

This is a fascinating field of inquiry, concerning the natural bonds by which the coherence of societies is preserved. The question is susceptible to no single or simple answer. For the devices which societies in all times have adopted to help maintain their structures have been many and varied.

Only comparatively rarely are the members of a society of many-celled creatures held together by actual physical bonds, as they are in the Portuguese man-of-war. No such obvious bonds unite the colonies of social insects, the families of birds, or the societies of men. To all superficial appearance, the members of these communities are relatively remote from one another. Compared to the polyps of a coral reef, they have a remarkable degree of individual freedom. Correspondingly, the cohesiveness of their societies would appear to be relatively low.

This is true only in part. Closer examination will disclose bonds of coherence among the members of such societies which, while less evident than actual physical linkage, are extraordinarily vital in maintaining social solidarity. An unusually clear example of such a force is the pattern known as trophallaxis—the mutual exchange of nourishment between members of a community—which does much to determine the character and maintain the integrity of many insect societies.

Perhaps the simplest expression of trophallaxis is to be found among certain termites. Termites are typically wood dwellers, and their principal food consists of woody tissue. This cellulose diet is not easy to obtain. While the termite is surrounded by wood, the ligneous tissue is tough and difficult to rasp off and to masticate. Moreover, it is of such low nutritive value that the individual termite must consume large quantities of it to survive and grow. Thus termites are extremely economical of the supplies which have been rasped off and partially digested. In their nests the gastric contents of every individual are passed on from one member of the community to another until there is little nourishment left in them. This is trophallaxis in its simplest form.

The significance of this simple sharing of food in the termite community, both in maintaining its integrity and in shaping its evolution, is hard to exaggerate. It creates a strong bond between individuals at the psychological level. It means that in its nest and among its fellows the individual termite will have access to a store of partly prepared food which would not otherwise be available. In consequence the nest and its nest mates will exert a strong attraction. Even more important, perhaps, is the fact that this exchange of food creates a chemical bond between individuals. Through it they are connected at the physiological level no less than are the individual cells of a mushroom. A splendid opportunity is provided for the diffusion from one individual to another of substances which may be of great importance in the colonial economy.

The evidence for the actual existence and function of chemicals diffused in this way among the members of a termite colony is meager, but it is definitely suggestive. The existence of such an exchange and its importance at both physiological and psychological levels are powerfully suggested by the further complex evolution of trophallaxis in the higher reaches of insect societies. For example, among the most advanced termites the colony is markedly affected by chemical bonds between its members of a much more elaborate nature than those involved in the simple exchange of food between individuals. Here the royal castes, and possibly the supplementary reproductive members of the community also, exude certain substances over the surface of the body which are eagerly sought after by the workers.

What these substances are is not at present known. But so avidly do the workers crave them that they will tear strips of epidermis from the swollen body of the queen in their frantic eagerness to secure the tidbits. The obese and lethargic queens of some of the African termite species, confined for life in small cells deep within the enormous mounds that stud the veldt country, and constantly surrounded by rings of expectant workers licking and cleaning them and carrying away the eggs as they appear, are often scarred from end to end where bits of skin have been torn from their bodies. This aspect of trophallaxis forms a far more powerful and more subtly significant bond than the mere exchange of food between worker termites.

In the first place, the substances which are sought by these means are so unique and so highly esteemed that they form a most potent psychological attachment between the worker and its colony. Nowhere else can the worker find these substances which it craves with the unreasoning intensity of a narcotic addict. Secondly, these substances are obtainable in quantity primarily from the royal pair. This serves sharply to distinguish the perfect egg-laying caste on the horizon of the worker. The colony is thus bonded in a polar manner to its royal couple rather than throughout its mass. Third, there is some evidence that the exuded substances are produced by the termite queen roughly in proportion to the amount of food she consumes. Since the queen can seek no food for herself, the workers may be early conditioned by the fact that the more food they bring the more exudate they receive. This marked incentive for the care of the queen is reinforced by the fact that if well fed she will produce more eggs. These also are highly attractive objects to the attendant workers, probably because of features of odor, taste, or texture.

At the other end of the insect series—in the social wasps and ants—trophallaxis has been developed in a more complex and yet more interesting way. It has been elaborated and extended to influence the relations between the adults and the immature members of the community in a most significant fashion. From the time they are hatched, the young members of a termite colony are relatively independent. They can run about like colts, and they can feed themselves from an early age. Many of the higher termites lay up stores of specially prepared food for the very young members of their community, but this is as far as parental care is carried. Among the wasps and ants, by way of contrast, the young are helpless grubs. They must be intimately cared for and fed from birth to maturity by their older nurses. In cementing and perpetuating this relation, trophallaxis becomes exceedingly important.

The larvae of most wasps and ants produce exudates which, like those of the queen termite, are eagerly sought by the workers. Among ants, these substances are apparently produced over most of the body surface and are licked off by the adults as they tend and fondle the young. Among the social wasps, the larvae are confined for life in their narrow cells and are not easily reached. Their exudates appear to be produced in a salivary fluid which is licked from their mouths by the nurses. As with the termite queen, the ant and the wasp larvae produce the freest flow of exudates when they are well nourished, and this circumstance offers the nurses a powerful incentive to feed them regularly and well.

As a rule, the young ant or wasp yields up its reward whenever food is placed before it. In times of scarcity, however, the nurses may demand the reward when no food is provided, and to a degree, they will succeed in securing it. Ants will roll their thin and hungry larvae over and over, seeking to extract the last drop of reward. Wasp nurses will pull their young grubs halfway out of their cells and then roughly jam them back again in a frantic effort to aid the reluctant flow of nectar. The larvae will respond to this rough treatment until they become famished and dried almost to waferlike flakes. There can be no doubt that this larval supply of rewards acts as a most potent attractive force binding the individual ant or wasp worker to the community in which it was born.

Nor is this exchange of reward confined to adult and young. Adult wasps on their combs are constantly feeding one another with salivary secretions or with the regurgitated contents of their crops. Among higher ants, the process has been elaborated and stereotyped and has become the basis for much of their communication. When a young ant first hatches, it is ravenously hungry, for it has taken no food since it spun its cocoon. Accordingly, it approaches an older sister to secure nourishment. As a larva it has been accustomed, whenever a worker nurse appeared, to uncoiling and working its mouth parts energetically, stimulating the adult to feed it. It behaves in the same general fashion now. But it is no longer a larva. It still works its mouth parts frantically, but it now has acquired legs, and the first pair of these share in the excitement.

The forelegs move rapidly up and down, sometimes stroking the cheeks of the older individual which is being solicited. This is a signal which is well recognized by the older ant. A drop of regurgitated food appears, and this the neophyte immediately imbibes. As the young ant grows older, it gradually suppresses some of this adolescent excitement. More important, it learns to integrate the whole business of food-begging into a stereotyped procedure which will instantly be recognized as a demand by all the fellow-members of the community. Finally, it becomes able to detect the signals of other ants which seek food from it, and to co-operate in providing the desired nourishment. Thus there is set up an intimately co-operative relationship among workers which acts not only as a subtle and a powerful bond of colonial solidarity, but forms an important basis for the communicatory function.

As with the termites, the bonds of trophallaxis do much more among ants than generally to unite the worker members to each other and to the young. They also serve to emphasize the role of the queen. For the old ant queen is usually fed entirely by the worker personnel of the colony. She is therefore constantly demanding food from the workers, and in return providing them with eggs, which are highly attractive objects. There is also some suggestion that the queen ant, like the queen termite, rewards her attendants with exudates, or at least with attractive odors, in response to the attentions which they lavish upon her.

Trophallaxis is certainly one of the most important bonds contributing to the solidarity of the insect colony, to the colonial associations of vertebrates, and even—to a degree—to human associations. But it cannot be the only bond. For among many of the primitive ants the structure of the digestive system is such that regurgitation is impossible and the bond of trophallaxis appears to be largely lacking among adults, although it may subsist between adults and young. Yet the colonies of such ants, though crude in many ways, are yet very stable. Among those semisocial wasps which seal up their young in the cells shortly after they are hatched from the eggs, almost all contact between the attendants and their nurses is early lost. In cases such as these, other stabilizing factors for the community must be involved. One such force is certainly that remote physical and psychic bond centering in the nest. So important is the nest as a bond in the existence of communities of multicellular organisms that the evolution of its function may be considered in some detail.

The story begins with a simple depression in the earth, such as might be excavated by a male sunfish at nesting time, or by a solitary young queen ant about to found a colony. The material is ready at hand. It is neither gathered nor physiologically evolved.

The modification of the site may be as slight as that made by a brooding nighthawk on a metropolitan gravel roof, yet there are psychological ties which bind the solitary organism to this chosen place which, primitive and elemental though they may be, are among the most significant of all the coherent forces of the social way. The homing tern will fly many weary miles and overcome serious difficulties to regain the crude nest-hollow of its selection. The solitary hunting wasp, having captured its prey, will brave the greatest hazards to return to its simple hole in the ground, though it contain but a single egg. The phenomenon is akin, perhaps, to the love of the familiar—be it of home or an established pattern of habit—and the dread of the unfamiliar with its associated fear of pain, which is so prominent a feature in human society.

The transition from this situation, in which a solitary individual or a single pair builds the nest and rears a family, to that in which the whole maturing family take part in the construction and enlarge and modify the structure is short. There is a whole group of beetles, including the so-called ambrosia beetles and the tachigalia beetles, which illustrates this stage. All of them are burrowers in wood. The nest, consisting of a mesh of interwoven and branched galleries, is usually started by a parent individual or pair. The young beetle grubs, like their parents, are for the most part wood borers, and soon after they are hatched their work contributes materially to the growing nest structure. Eventually they transform to adults. But they do not leave the colony. Instead, their further activities become a most positive benefit. The nest grows apace in extent and intricacy. It is only when the beetles have become so numerous that they are unduly crowded that the stabilizing function of the nest weakens, and individuals wander away by twos and threes to establish new structures of their own. The nest of a young ant or termite colony performs a function almost identical with that of the semisocial beetles, except that the community which it shelters, integrated as it is by many additional ties, is of far more permanent character.

The next step in this evolution represents a rather momentous development. Now comes the first hint of the use of physiologically evolved substances in nest building. The nest is actually fashioned, though still built largely of materials which occur naturally. In one genus of the solitary wasps—*Zethus*—mud has been abandoned as too crude a material for building the beautiful pots of clay that are its brood cells. The exquisite little nests of this creature consist of a series of tubular cells fashioned of small bits of leaves or moss cemented together with an oral secretion. Some of the solitary bees are likewise given to building their brood cells of such materials as leaflets or tiny bits of flowers, skillfully arranged like shingles on a roof. Or again, they may employ chewed-up plant materials, producing a secretion which hardens into a thin film so tenuous and yet so tough as to resemble goldbeaters' skin.

How tenaciously the little families of the primitively social Philippine wasp *Stenogaster* cling together on the fragile swaying rod of twisted cells that is their home! It would be hard to imagine a more tenuous structure than such a colony consisting only of a mother and a few mature daughters. Almost all of the ties to social life which reinforce the higher social bees and wasps are lacking. The maturing young are fully physiologically endowed as reproductive females, so that there is no obvious dependence of the daughters on the colony. The bonds of communication are simple and feebly developed. And so, although it would be hard to imagine a less pretentious nest than the little tube of braided combs so lightly built that it would seem as if the merest jungle breeze must shatter it from the tip of a pendent fern, its role in promoting the stability of the colony is decisive. In the strong attachment to it that is mutual to mother and young is provided an effective focal point for the infant communal life.

The full burgeoning of the nest as a factor of cohesiveness in society becomes fully manifest among the higher social wasps and bees. Here the attachment of the colony to its nest may be so strong that it rarely deserts to form a new nest except under very unusual circumstances. A colony of yellow jackets, for instance, is utterly lost if its paper nest is destroyed. The more modestly developed communities of the eaves wasps—*Polistes*—disperse readily if their single comb is removed. The stingless Melipone bees of the American tropics are profoundly disorganized if their nests are devastated. The hive of the honeybee, with its rich stores of nectar and pollen, is as much a supply of coveted food for the worker as is the community of potentially regurgitating fellow-members for the worker ant. Thus to the psychological attachment which all social insects have toward their nests there is added the powerful incentive of food rewards. In fact, the hive has become so essential to the worker honeybee that the loss of it may endanger the very life of the individual.

Various other ties bind the structures of the true societies. One of these is communication. There are no insect associations known in which a definite caste specializes in the transmission of messages or in the co-ordination of the parts to the whole. While every individual is a potential communicant with every other one, the messages transmitted are crude and of limited content. As a rule, they achieve their effect by arousing an over-all generalized stimulation in the receiver of the message. Once the attention of the stimulated individual is fixed on the purveyor of information, the remaining effect is achieved by example or by tangible demonstration of the situation at hand.

Thus when a termite colony is invaded, the soldiers may excitedly rap their heads against the walls of the galleries. This stimulates their fellows to a general alarm but gives them no specific information, so far as can be determined. Certain arboreal ants spread alarms by tapping in myriads on the leaves until they produce the effect of a patter of rain. This action, however, apparently merely increases the awareness of their fellows that something undefined is out of the ordinary. Worker bees returning from a rich foraging expedition will dance excitedly on the comb of the hive, arousing the colony to a fever pitch of generalized excitement. By paying close attention to the original messenger they are able to locate the rich stores which she has found. Similarly ants, when returning from foraging expeditions, will enter the nest precipitately and there behave in a characteristically exciting manner. The original discoverer will soon re-emerge with a dozen followers and lead them to the discovery.

No experimental evidence has ever been obtained that any abstract ideas are conveyed by this behavior. Recent investigations, it is true, have suggested that a remarkably detailed picture may be conveyed in the case of bees; specific information may also sometimes flow from one ant to another, as when the informed individual actually transports a sister to the new site of a nest or to a food supply. But this crude process is akin to the generalized stimulatory action mentioned earlier. Extensive studies have demonstrated that individual ants are capable of considerable adaptive behavior and of a fair degree of learning, particularly during the early portions of their lives; no specific details, however, can be conveyed by an ant to its fellows, except in so far as the uninformed individuals actually imitate their preceptors. Thus the fruits of the life and labor of an individual social insect must perish with it. Only the general stimulus-pattern—the rapping of the termite head, the dance of the worker bee, the excited solicitation movements of the hungry worker ant—remain as a colonial heritage. This situation has had a retarding effect upon the development of the finer levels of co-ordination within insect societies. In part it may account for the slow progress of the changes which have been wrought within them during the many millennia of their evolutionary existence.

This method of communication by stimulation, which often achieves surprising results in an adaptive sense in an ant, is strikingly exemplified among giant colonies, such as those of the Doryline Driver ants of the genus *Eciton*. The Drivers are wholly carnivorous and in consequence live as perpetual nomads, making predatory raids upon the insect life about them. They establish temporary bivouacs, varying in situation with the species. These are constructed against logs or within hollow tree trunks of the jungle. They are most remarkable in that the building material of which they are constructed may consist, not of earth or wood, but of the living bodies of the ants themselves. The colony hangs like a giant quiescent swarm of bees, the mass penetrated by galleries and chambers within which the queen and the brood are retained. In some Doryline species these nests may comprise masses of ants as large as a bushel basket.

Until the time arrives for a migration, these immense clusters hang almost completely inert and with little sign that they are alive. Yet a close inspection reveals a slight but constant movement, which continuously brings to the surface of the mass bits of discarded food, empty cocoons, or the larval exuviae of hatching or pupating young ants, all to be dropped onto the temporary refuse piles which surround the bivouac. In and out of these inert but living galleries pass columns of intensely active raiders. The columns fan far out into the jungle in a complicated network of channels that throws its toils over a large area of forest floor. Within this domain every stick, stone, and grass blade is canvassed for living insect prey. Quite as constantly, columns return laden with booty, to pour into the depths of the nest where the larvae and young ants are held.

The behavior of these communities is cyclic. During the rainy season the colony of *Eciton hamatum* exhibits a peak of raiding activity of seventeen days. During this time the entire organization migrates at the end of nearly every day. The immobile units gradually become active, and the nest itself literally dissolves and flows out along the raiding trails. Finally it gradually re-forms at some appropriate spot, first as a small knot of ants, then as a gradually growing swarm, until a new nest and base of operation is established. During this eighteen-day period the energy of the insects reaches a peak and begins to decline. Toward the end the raids fall off sharply, and the daily migration may be omitted once or twice. Finally the colony ceases to migrate at all and enters its quiescent period, which lasts approximately for another three weeks. The raids themselves decrease in frequency still further, and on some days, at the depth of this depression of activity, they too may be missed altogether. But eventually the vigor of the raids begins again to increase, until at last they become so extended that the nest flows away to a new site. The migratory period has begun anew.

The causes of this periodicity have been investigated, and it is here that the diffuse character of the transmission of stimuli within the insect colony is most vividly illustrated. Brood production by the queen is limited to but a few days. In this period laying occurs rapidly and enormous numbers of eggs accumulate. But after this short burst the ovaries shrink, and no more eggs are produced until the next cycle. These cycles are so spaced that at the time of egg deposition an older class of brood is present as recently spun cocoons. The eggs hatch before the cocoons begin to produce adult young ants. During the time that the pupae of the older brood are quiet in their cocoons and while the younger generation are still very small larvae, there is little movement in the colony. The maximum depression of community activity probably occurs at this time.

As the hatching time of the cocoons approaches the pupae within them become restless. They squirm and stretch, and their restlessness is communicated to their nurses. At first these aroused adults merely cluster about the writhing cocoons. Soon, however, they begin to gnaw at them, then actually to open them and to extract the young ants, which immediately become the objects of great solicitude. Excitement is exhibited in the colony almost as soon as the hatching process commences, not only in the adults which attend the cocoons, but in others farther afield. This occurs evidently by a sort of chain process in which the stimulation is conveyed from adult to adult.

Raiding picks up. The foraging columns become larger, their expeditions range farther afield, and increased booty pours into the nest. As the numbers of hatching cocoons increase, the excitement mounts. Finally, as thousands of cocoons daily yield up an ever-welling stream of young ants, the infection of excitement becomes so intense that a mass foray is initiated and the equilibrium of the community is upset. As the hours pass the raiding columns fail to return.

The center of gravity of the community has been shifted. Bit by bit the nest dissolves and flows outward upon the trails, accompanied by its new-hatched and still bewildered young adults. The larval members of the younger brood are trundled along slung beneath the bodies of the workers. Each night the site of the bivouac is shifted. The raiding increases in intensity as the new larvae rapidly become larger, more active, and more demanding.

Finally, these larvae begin to spin their cocoons. All at once they are transformed to quiet, ovoid objects which no longer stimulate the workers to any extent. As more of the larvae enter this condition of inactivity the vigor of the colonial forays drops off sharply. The nightly shift of bivouac is omitted. The community enters upon its stationary period. The few remaining larvae become enclosed in their silken envelopes. The ovaries of the queen distend once more and a new group of eggs appears. Now there is no brood in the nest save the inert eggs and the equally inert cocoons. With no stimulation from active larvae on the one hand or from struggling, hatching pupae on the other, the colony gradually becomes passive. Finally even the daily raid is omitted. The community enters the depressed portion of its cycle, from which it will slowly be revived, first by the hatching of the cocoons and later by the rapid growth of the new young larvae.

In this process we see an exquisitely adaptive performance. Yet the mechanism by which the cycle is achieved appears to reside primarily in the transmission of a generalized state of excitement, initiated by the stimuli exerted by the active brood on the ants immediately surrounding them and conditioned by the isolated and individual responses of the colony members. These stimuli are apparently propagated by contacts from ant to ant throughout the mass.

It is clear that communication in insect societies is necessarily limited in both character and scope. The individual's learning processes and its ability to recombine its experiences are restricted as compared with those of most vertebrates. More serious is the fact that the individual insects seem largely incapable of imparting the qualitative character of their experiences. So far as can be detected, they can only stimulate others in a general way to an activity conditioned by the mental state of the recipient. Yet, although insect societies have made exceedingly slow progress relative to the social evolution of vertebrates, they are not static. Witness the subtle advances of the most socially advanced over the most primitive termites, and of the honeybee over *Allodape*.

These advances involve mental and psychic behavior quite as much as they do physical organization. In the adaptive sense, the highly specialized communal insects certainly display the results of a form of social adaptation which has been transmitted from ancestral forms and has slowly become elaborated within the species. In part and in important part, this transmission is hereditary and involves as well the successive elaboration and integration of instincts through mutations. In part, it may arise anew in each generation through the individual learning process in the social milieu, for the young ant or bee certainly learns much in the first formative days of its adult life from observation and imitation of the patterns about it. It would be strange if innovations were not occasionally introduced in this way which spread through the community by repeated imitation. This, however, could be true only within a *single* colony. The innovation could never survive from one colony to another unless the young queen transmitted it in her behavior pattern—an exceedingly unlikely event.

What of the forces of cohesion in that most interesting and important social structure of all—the communities of men? Human society is in many ways quite different from any other social structure in the world. This general difference of form penetrates to many specific features of structure. Yet despite wide differences in the ties which bind the societies of men and those of other social organisms, there are parallels which are interesting and not without significance.

Most of these similarities relate to the more primitive reaches of human social organization. To a very considerable degree, normal men are instinctively specialized to the communal way of life quite as much as are the social insects, though both the nature of this adaptation and the kind of society to which it applies are very different. The gratification of most normal men at appropriate social approval, the antipathy they have for a life of total solitude, and the curious psychological alterations which so frequently supervene when they are forced to lead such lives—all these give powerful evidence that man too is dominated by a strong instinctive drive for the permanent company of his kind and must have it for his individual well-being.

Evidence is not lacking that trophallaxis plays an important part in reinforcing the solidarity of human societies. Its expression is, however, somewhat different from that found among the communal insects. In the purely physical sense, the exchange of nourishment or of other physically attractive rewards plays an important part in solidifying the social relations of many vertebrates. It is to be seen in the feeding of pigeons by their mates, and in the feeding of predigested food to the young by both parents among many species of grain-feeding birds. The nourishment of the young by milk provides a powerful bond in cementing the early family solidarity of many mammals. And there seems good evidence that the young of such creatures, like those of the social invertebrates, in their turn provide pleasing stimuli which serve as physical and psychic rewards for the attention which they receive.

Many of these modes of behavior are carried over into human society. They certainly play a predominant part in the shaping of family relations and in the early conditioning of human young. But they appear in a far more elaborated, conspicuous, and probably more important form, both on the psychic plane and in the larger society which comprehends the adult human community. The mutual mental exchange between the adult members of a human community in the form of news or gossip brings subtle satisfactions to both doner and receiver. As old as human social living, its importance as a cohesive force is not to be underestimated. The process of bargaining—also as old as the communities of men —brings satisfactions of the same sort and obviously constitutes a binding tie of great significance. The function of the nest as represented by the house or, at a higher level of human society, by the village, the town, or the great city, is evidently extremely important in ensuring the solidarity and the continuity of the societies of men far beyond the span of any one generation. Even the role of specialization, so prominent as a binding force in insect associations, is not wanting among men, although it affects primarily the psychological rather than the physical realm. The list of such similarities might be greatly extended.

Communication in human society is of course a vastly more complex matter than among invertebrates, but it is no less important as a binding tie on this account. It is, in fact, far more exquisitely adapted to promoting solidarity and permitting rapid internal co-ordination, and far broader in scope and more dynamic in character, than in any other social organism. This arises in part from the much greater range and flexibility of the mind of the individual —a characteristic conspicuous among all higher vertebrates and culminating in man. In part also it arises from the ability of man— alone among living things—to communicate complex ideas directly from individual to individual.

Despite the tremendous heights to which human communication has been carried, thanks to the innate potentials inherent in man alone, it nevertheless presents in its more primitive reaches certain significant similarities to the patterns of other social organisms. While complex ideation and the transmission of elaborate thought patterns are possible to man, he still responds quickly to the transmission of simple stimuli, which may not be at all unlike those motivating the members of the Doryline colony. No reasoned discourse, however effectively presented, can so quickly or so profoundly move a group of mothers as the cry of an infant in distress. No crowd, unless it has been carefully conditioned, will galvanize to an orator as it will to the cry of "Fire!" No other advertising can succeed so well as that which simplifies its concept into a single word or picture, and stimulates a short, repetitive, rewarded chain of action. No social stimulus is so effective among men as the simple one which calls into play direct trains of deeply instinctive thought and action. The monotonous rhythm of the drum evokes the most powerful mass reactions in primitive peoples, though no single word or formed idea may be conveyed. The world has just passed through the most overwhelming demonstration that has ever been seen of the portentous power of mass hysteria—of the awesome force of unformed hate and fear stimulated by mass propaganda.

All the elemental reactions so characteristic of communication in invertebrate societies are also to be found in the societies of humans. Upon them has been grafted another structure far more delicately modulated and fraught with infinitely greater possibilities. But it is important to remember that while primitive elements are frequently overlaid in evolution, they nevertheless persist tenaciously. Often they form the actual basis of more complex elaborations. Thus all the finer attributes of man—his aesthetic appreciation, his specialized communication of that appreciation in poetry and music, the fine modulation of his speech and his writing, and his mathematical insight—may yet be intimately related to much simpler and more elemental forms of communication.

Moreover, as the institution of parasitism so well shows, evolutionary trends from the complex to the simple can occur quite as readily as in the opposite direction. Thus no civilization of man is exempt from the danger of a reversion to barbarism. The latent power of the ancient, the primitive, and the deep-seated should not be underestimated, and man must be ever vigilant that in his social evolution the finer elements are not progressively replaced by simpler and coarser ones.

Diffuse communication occurring throughout the social structure, analogous to the process in the Doryline colony, is inherent in the life of the human community. This is in evidence at the highest as well as at the lowest levels. Village gossip, rumor, the gradual dissemination of news—all these fall into this category. All of them elicit stimuli by a slow and continuous process until eventually the entire social group has been alerted.

But in addition there are distinct signs in human social organization of a specialization of the function of communication which is novel. There are few human societies so primitive as to lack the professional storyteller, the orator, the messenger, or the crier or beater of drums. His daily work involves a more than ordinary preoccupation with the art of communication, and his special function is to alert or inform the community. There is no counterpart for this situation to be found among invertebrate societies, though the warden of a flock of crows vaguely suggests such a development among the vertebrates. In modern society the intensive development of the art of communication—in journalism, in advertising, in public address—has definitely tended to transform this communication net into a highly organized chain. If speed and accuracy of communication is the criterion of merit of a society, then today's world community of mankind far excels any other form of association among living things.

CHAPTER 10

Three Societies

THE TWO great principles manifested in the trends to complexity and simplicity are well-nigh universal in their effect upon the evolution of societies, as they are upon the evolution of all life. Human societies no less than the societies of other living things are subject to these grand influences and reflect their effects in broadly similar fashion. The trend to complexity is a reflection of the pressure of adaptation and natural selection impressed upon societies as it is upon non-social life by the demands of an environment. That environment is the earth as a whole, which has itself grown more complex down the ages. Its opposite, the trend to simplification and specialization, is in turn a reflection of special aspects of that environment upon life and upon societies alike—the effects of special conditions that are monotonous or rigid and unyielding in their specific demands, such as those of heat or cold or drought, or of the host-parasite relation.

The third principle, that of integration, is less universal in its application. This principle now demands a closer scrutiny. Like complexity and specialization, it is an adaptive device in the survival of societies. But it is a device that has been adopted only by certain kinds of societies. Conspicuous among them are such integrated groups as the Siphonophorans and the social insects. In the whole vast realm of family and associative societies, the trend to integration is but rarely and feebly expressed. Indeed, there is good reason to believe that in many cases it may actually be inimical to them in evolution. And since human society is integrative in only one specialized aspect—as will presently be developed—it is important to examine somewhat more closely the whole associative social way.

Here is the core of the matter. Nearly all the superficial comparisons which are made between human and non-human societies take as their text the identity of the resemblances between social man and some of the spectacular integrated non-human social organizations—particularly those of the social insects. The postulates are these: Because human and non-human societies alike show the impress of the trends to complexity and to specialization and hence face similar evolutionary dangers, it has too often been assumed that the trend to integration affects them in similar ways, and that if human societies are to survive they must go the way of the insect colony in evolution, exhibiting tighter and tighter integration, with correspondingly less and less of individual autonomy. In the course of natural evolution the member of the human society, like that of the insect colony—so the argument runs—is to approach the role of the parasite, to become increasingly dependent, to lose more and more of individual competence. The integrated society has long been the text for theses upon the merits—or the inevitability—of totalitarian organization. But nature is not so simple.

The societies of the world are of divers kinds and shapes. Many attempts have been made to classify them. Most of these have encountered various difficulties inherent in the almost impossible task of selecting suitable criteria. Many categories have been defined. The simple classification here adopted, which divides all societies into three broad classes—the integrated, the family, and the associative—is not intended to be either comprehensive or precise. It is based entirely upon their evolutionary aspects, their origins, and their modes of development, and is specifically designed to illuminate these particular problems.

In this general classification the phrase *family societies* is used to include all those social groupings which consist of one or two parents and a brood of their young, dwelling together until the young are partially or wholly grown, and then gradually drifting apart. Thus family societies in general are relatively evanescent. Typically, all the members of such societies are genetically related. All of them are capable of breeding.

Integrated societies, on the other hand, are much more permanent. They also consist of one or more parents and one or more generations of descendants, so that, typically, most of the members of the society are more or less closely related. But unlike the family, only a few members of the integrated society are capable of maintaining an independent existence, and only a few of them can reproduce themselves effectively. The rest are non-reproductive, are highly specialized to the society, and approach the status of cogs in a machine.

The *associative society* differs from both of these in important particulars. It is the loose flock or herd, the members of which are not usually closely related by ties of blood. The associative society is characteristically evanescent. It is often formed from impulses of mere gregariousness and dissolves when the circumstances calling it into being have vanished. At its simplest, it is a fleeting aggregation like the passengers on an ocean liner. But in its more extreme reaches, it attains impressive proportions and becomes of great importance.

Integrated societies can arise in evolution from family forms. This, indeed, seems to have been their usual genesis in such groups as the Siphonophorans and among the social insects. Now human society depends heavily upon the family, and throughout all of human social evolution the family has played a dominant role. Why, then, is there not danger that the human family might develop into the kind of integrated, close-knit social situation represented by the social insects? There are a number of cogent answers to this question. Here only one or two of a strictly biological nature need be considered.

Not all the conditions are fully known under which the remarkable and rather rare evolution of a family into a highly organized integrated society can take place. But three of them can be stated with relative certainty. In the first place, the founding member or members of such a society must attain considerable longevity so that they may survive many broods of their descendants, and thus live contemporaneously with them. This, for example, is the case with the ant or bee queen. Second, this founding member must be immensely fecund, capable of giving rise to hundreds or thousands or tens of thousands of progeny—again like the termite or bee or ant queen. Third, the reproductive members of the tightly integrated community, from which new communities can arise, must comprise a decided minority of the total population, and the rest must be non-reproducing, or at any rate must be members which do not ordinarily found new communities.

Now man—or any other warm-blooded vertebrate, for that matter—is biologically incapable of fulfilling these conditions. No warm-blooded vertebrates in the course of their evolution seem ever to have developed either the fecundity or the differences in longevity within a species that form essential parts of the biological basis for the integrated societies of the invertebrates. Unlike the social insects, intracommunal selection among individuals rather than intercommunal selection between whole social groups is the rule among the vertebrates—a great and significant difference in the mechanisms of their evolution. Biologically, it would seem pretty certain that human beings simply cannot develop in the direction of the social insects. In addition there are, of course, powerful factors, in the realm of psychology and the mind, which prevent mankind from forming typical integrated societies. But one need go no further than this biological impasse to show that the chance of the human family ever duplicating the evolution to a huge integrated society is, for practical purposes, negligible.

What, now, of the associative form of social living, so widespread in nature? The black flocks of starlings that twist against the winter city sky, the swarms of midges dancing in spring on the margins of the ponds, the tent caterpillars in their communal webs, the salmon runs in turbulent rivers, migrating wild fowl on their continental flyways—all these are examples, in varying degree, of the simpler levels of the associative society. So also are the tropical communal spiders which spin webs sometimes twenty feet across, the masses of ladybird beetles that one may discover under stones or the bark of trees in December, the flocks of southward-migrating Monarch butterflies, or the locust hordes that plagued the Mormons.

Perhaps the most striking example of this kind of organization is to be found at the unicellular level of life. Among the curious group of fungi known as the slime molds is a strange genus called *Dictyostelium,* of the Acrasiales. Individuals of *Dictyostelium* begin life as single resting spores, which may remain alive in the inert condition for some time. But if they fall into a suitable warm and humid environment, each spore splits and germinates. There is then disclosed, not a young mold of the conventional form, but a cell which is essentially an amoeba. This young cell, amoeba-like, wanders away through its medium, changing its shape frequently, and engulfing bacteria as it goes. For a number of generations it grows and divides by fission, like any other amoeba, until a considerable number of individuals has appeared. At a certain point in this process of growth and division, however, a curious and striking change takes place. By twos and threes, and then in crowds, the amoebas begin to stream together to a common point, and to fuse their individual bodies into an elongated, sausage-like mass which may come to be as much as two millimeters in length. Compared with one of the component cells of this strange association, these are prodigious dimensions.

When this sausage, called a plasmodium, is complete, it proceeds to exhibit a motility and individuality of its own, moving from the place of its formation like a single animal. Under the microscope, it can be seen that while this motion is accomplished by the movements of individual component cells, these movements are now well co-ordinated to produce a unitary effect.

After a day or more, depending upon the local conditions, the sausage ceases its movement, becomes fixed to one spot, and, turning into a rounded mass, assumes an upright position with an upwardly thrust pointed tip. Within the mass a core is gradually formed, and the rounded blob of protoplasm becomes extended upward. Bit by bit the core lengthens and eventually comes to form a long and conspicuous stalk, raised well above the surface of the medium. At the top of the stalk is a rounded knob of constituent amoebae, like the head of a pin. Ultimately the individual cells in this knob become surrounded with tough resistant walls and form new spores. From these, in time, new amoebae will emerge to repeat the cycle, swimming, feeding, growing, coming together and fusing once more to form a new plasmodium, and later a new stalk and head.

These remarkable organisms may serve as a model, at the level of the cellular aggregate, of the associative society. It will be remembered that the associative society typically consists of a group of individuals, not necessarily in close relation genetically, which have come together into a temporary association after they have been for a period in a relatively solitary state. Ultimately such an association dissolves, some or all of its members resuming their solitary state. The cell associations of *Dictyostelium* fulfill all of these conditions.

Associative societies are not highly specialized and tightly integrated communities having a strongly developed individuality. They are primitive, flexible, generalized. Within them the endowment and the potentialities for independent living of the individual have remained at a high level. As in the family type of society, the individual is not very strictly regimented, as compared with individuals in the advanced integrated societies. Rarely if ever is the separation of an individual from an association of this sort fatal to it, as it may be to the individual body cell of a plant or animal or to the individual worker honeybee. In fact, it is quite characteristic of associative societies that they dissolve periodically, like the association of *Dictyostelium*, or a flock of migrating birds when it has reached its nesting grounds.

Thus the individual components are regularly released for periods of independent existence before they are again united. In comparison even with families, associative societies are extremely amorphous in the sense that they can readily be divided into parts and later reunited, or combined with other associative groups. A flock of birds or of Monarch butterflies traveling southward will freely augment its numbers with additions from day to day. These newcomers will be received with tolerance by the society sometimes even if they are of different species, regardless of whether the new arrivals are individually known to the flock.

Only the most tolerant of family societies will permit such liberties. And contrast the situation in the associative group with the utter intolerance of the integrated society—the colonies of some species of bees or ants, for instance—to individuals which are not by birth members of the same group, even though they are of the same species and so alike that the human eye has difficulty in distinguishing them. The family society clearly contains the potentiality of building high and impermeable walls around itself, which may become very strongly developed in the integrated society. But in the typical associative society such walls are virtually lacking.

Concomitant with this situation, no case of highly organized warfare seems ever to have been recorded between animal communities of the associative type, although a primitive concerted action in attack and defense, such as that of the crow flock or the musk-ox herd, is not uncommon. Indeed, the loose and ill-defined structure characteristic of associative societies would make such concerted activity virtually impossible on any very extensive scale. Among integrated societies, large-scale and highly organized warfare is of course all too common. Such are the vicious and often long-continued wars between communities of ants, which may lead to the extermination of all but one colony in a restricted area. Carried out on a global scale by such conquistadors as *Pheidole megacephala* and *Iridomyrmex humilis*, they can lead to the extermination of whole species of unfortunate victims.

Among the selective factors affecting the evolution of the

primitive family are a number of causes which tend to militate in evolution against its further internal integration. Notable among these is its impermanence with respect to the individual. Another important potential impediment to the transformation of the family society into the integrated form is that, so long as all the members of a family group are potentially able to breed, it is only comparatively rarely that mutations can become established through natural selection which will at the same time react to the detriment of the individual and to the benefit of the group. It is only when the fecundity of a few individuals has become exaggerated, and when breeding in the community has become largely restricted to those individuals, that such mutations, leading to the dominance of the society over the individuals composing it, can be established in significant numbers.

On the other hand, certain properties of the family society may, under appropriate conditions, lead in evolution toward a heightened integration of its internal structure. Notable among these are the genetic kinship that typically exists among its members and the fact that, born as they are into a common social environment, the family members are early conditioned to such surroundings and may be tempted to remain in them indefinitely. Moreover, once a certain degree of preliminary integration has been achieved within a family society, leading to a reduced capacity for individual living on the part of most of its members, strong selective forces come into play leading that integration to progress ever further until it culminates in the unitary society of the ant or termite colony.

All this would lead one to suspect what is in fact observed— first, that integrated societies have in general arisen from family forms; and second, that this spectacular transformation has occurred but rarely.

It is interesting to examine from the same viewpoint the potentialities for integration inherent in the associative way of life. They seem much reduced. Typically, the members of an associative society are born as solitary individuals. What conditioning they have to social existence tends to come in the mid-portion of their life-cycle rather than at the beginning. However, they may have been conditioned to communal living in general by a previous existence and rearing in family societies—and this point probably tends to make combinations of family and associative societies rather easy and rather common. Typically, also, the members of the associative group are not closely related individuals. They represent a much more genetically heterogeneous population than do the members of a typical family society. Finally, in the associative society every member is and tends to remain a potential parent. This further militates against the likelihood of the transformation of an associative into a highly integrated society.

The adaptive pressures on the associative society seem strongly and consistently against any close form of integration in evolution. Indeed, they contain few of the elements which would permit their development into integrated societies. No instances are known to me in which integrated societies can be shown to have arisen from such beginnings. There are cases, to be sure, where organisms living in family groups, several of which normally exist in close association, have given rise to later types living in typical integrated societies. In such cases, however, further analysis will show that the integrated society has actually arisen from the individual family rather than from the association of families.

On the other hand, it is evident that the adaptive pressures on the associative society operate strongly in the direction of over-all competence, self-sufficiency, and independence among the *individuals* composing them. The typical associative society, since it exhibits little internal specialization among its members, must rely for its survival upon the generalized capabilities of each of its component parts. This is in direct contrast to the integrated society, which relies upon an over-all advanced capacity resulting from the specialization of different social components in different directions. The figure of merit of an associative society, therefore, must lie in the accentuation rather than in the suppression of the generalized characteristics of competence and individuality among its members.

The philosophy of survival of an associative society thus seems exactly opposite to that of a society of the integrated type. In view of this, it is perhaps somewhat surprising to observe that large associative societies are quite as commonly found in nature as are the large integrated ones. Further, they are actually more commonly met with than those smaller, more primitive integrated societies which in the degree of their internal specialization more nearly approach the associative form. Associative societies are almost certainly as ancient in evolution as are integrated ones, if not more so.

All of these circumstances suggest, first, that the associative form of society is quite as successful in evolution as is the integrated one; and second, that associative and integrated societies do not come into competition for survival to the same degree as lowly and highly developed integrated forms do between themselves. In the language of the naturalist, these two social forms may occupy rather different and non-competitive ecological niches in nature.

In view of all this, it is not remarkable to find that the integrated and associative forms of society are very rarely if ever found in combination among the animals of the world. The very cohesiveness of the highly integrated society, the tremendous degree of interdependence among its members, and the intolerance of the group to alien intrusion, all militate strongly against the possibility of any such combination. On the other hand, the situation is quite different with respect to mixtures of the family and associative forms. However much they may differ in certain fundamental aspects of their constitution, family and associative societies are alike in the low extent of their internal co-ordination and in the relatively high level of independence among their members. They also resemble each other in that the component individuals of both types commonly spend a considerable portion of their life cycles as solitary individuals, and all of them are potential breeders.

These last characteristics open a promising avenue of partnership or "symbiosis," as it were, between family and associative social forms. For individuals conditioned to family living in their youth are quite likely, after they have spent some time as solitary adults, again to seek out the companionship of their own kind in mass and so to form associative societies. Moreover, associative societies provide environments in which the chances of individuals acquiring suitable mates and so of setting up new family societies are particularly good. Finally, once such pairs are formed and breeding, if they remain in communal association and thus perpetuate the mixture of the family and associative forms they have a good chance of retaining permanently all those advantages of the associative society which are inherent in the combined watchfulness and alertness and the pooled competences of a group of semi-independent individuals.

In view of these obvious compatibilities between associative and family societies, and the advantages inherent in their combination under suitable circumstances, it is not surprising to find that such combinations are rather widespread. Such mixtures are beautifully illustrated by the colony-nesting birds. The vast rookeries of noddies and terns, of albatrosses and frigate birds on the sandy atolls of tropical seas, the colonies of gulls and cormorants, guillemots, puffins, and gannets on the rocky isles of more polar oceans, the strange nesting "herds" of king and emperor penguins in Antarctica, are all examples of this sort of relationship. It reaches the height of its expression, perhaps, in the African sociable weaver bird *Philetaerus*. Here as many as two hundred pairs of birds may fuse their grass-woven nests into one gigantic mass which is protected from the rain by a communal rooflike structure.

Similar examples are to be found among the mammals. The colonies of prairie dogs and ground squirrels, the permanent herds of wild asses and zebras, of musk oxen and antelopes, of giraffes and elephants, the colonies of beavers, the communal flocks of macaque monkeys, and the troops of gibbons and perhaps of other primates relatively close to the line of human descent—all exhibit this same combination of types composed of mixtures of related and unrelated individuals.

Even among the solitary, cell-provisioning wasps and bees, which form typical family communities of mother and young, there are examples of mixtures of associative and family living. Females of the wasp genus *Bembex*, for example, excavate individual earthen burrows, each terminated by a cell which is provisioned with insect prey on which an egg is placed. After the egg has hatched, the mother continues to tend the cells. This, of course, is the typical behavior pattern of a solitary insect just after entering the first stage of evolution to the family society. Yet at the same time the adult females show a strong proclivity to congregate and to build their burrows in proximity, occasionally even constructing a single communal entrance for them, although they resent actual intrusion on their privacy by neighbors. This, in contrast, is the typical behavior of a solitary creature in the first stage of forming an associative union. The colony-like collection of individual burrows which results is thus neither a purely family nor a purely associative type of society. It is a most intimate mixture of the two, in which, possibly, the conditioning of each young wasp to the family society leads it later to congregate with other adults to form an associative one.

Cannot human society be viewed from the standpoint of its biological constitution as in essence a similar mixture of the family and associative forms? Is it not at base somewhat like a colony of sociable weaver birds or of beavers, or a community-dwelling of *Bembex*? The family-society portion of the human mixture then becomes the family itself, and will be found to have many of the characteristics typical of similar structures at primitive levels elsewhere. Thus all members of the human family are closely genetically related, as is true among typical family societies. Within both the primitive and the modern human family group the instinctive bonds of cohesiveness, the binding ties of family loyalty, are direct and strong. Further, ties of this particular sort are not readily extended beyond the family sphere. This loyalty is well indicated by the persistent cohesiveness of the human family as a unit at every social level, and the rarity with which alien adult members are adopted into it in most civilizations unless powerful external motivations lead to such adoptions as a social custom, as was the case, for instance, among various distinguished families of older China. In modern society even the adoption of infants into alien families is a comparatively rare event.

Finally, the members of a human family spend the early portions of their lives intimately within this social environment, but in the case of western civilization, they frequently leave at maturity to live for a time as relatively independent members of the associative group before establishing new families of their own. When the human family structure becomes more permanent than the individuals within it, and retains its structure unchanged for several generations, it may develop some of the qualities of the integrated society. On occasion this has occurred in the Orient. In all these respects the family society of man is comparable with more primitive family organizations the world over. It exhibits the ties that unite the family of tachigalia beetles, the specialization of duties of a pair of nesting hornbills, and the hostility of a family of nesting sparrows to outside groups.

Within historical times this human family unit has not advanced greatly in complexity of structure, in degree of organization, or in subordination of parts to the whole. Furthermore, there seems no reason to suppose that the modern family shows any great increase in specialization over the family of Piltdown or Java or Pekin or Cro-Magnon man. This emphasizes again the principle that specialization to integration is very unlikely to occur in human family societies, where the fecundity of each individual is comparatively low, and where most individuals tend, ultimately, to propagate. It seems safe to conjecture that the family society of man, like the vast majority of family societies in nature, has shown little or no tendency to proceed toward the integrated form in the course of human biological evolution. It is not in this area of his communal living that the great social changes characteristic of modern man have occurred.

On the associative side of communal living, however, human society presents a startling contrast to the relatively primitive organization of the family. Here it is that mankind is wholly unique. I know of no other organism which lives through a mixture of the family and associative social forms in which the associative type of social evolution approaches the family pattern in specialization or dominance, much less exceeds it. The nesting associations of the wasp genus *Bembex* are evanescent indeed beside the relatively close-knit social entity that is the individual female and her developing brood. Even the plasmodium of *Dictyostelium* is a temporary and shifting thing compared to the permanence of the nuclei which it contains and which will persist into the spore, into the amoeboid organism that hatches from it, and on into a new plasmodium, long after the older associative structure has vanished.

But in the societies of modern man the family, despite its antiquity, persistence, and relative cohesiveness, is by no means so clearly dominant over the associative structure which envelops it. In times of political crises, it is frequently the associative structure and not the family which commands the highest loyalty of men. So brother will fight with brother in internal civil war. So the bitternesses engendered within a family group by opposing political and social creeds, which may have reference only to the associative half of the society, can permanently rupture the smaller unit and leave its members with enduring bitterness.

In man—and in man alone—the associative structure is much more specialized than the family pattern. In sharp contrast to the slow-moving evolution of the ancient family type, it continues to evolve dynamically at a rate which today far outstrips the social development of any organism that earth has known.

Such is the special and the infinitely serious social problem of man. He is at once deeply adjusted to the family, to which he has been attached since ancient times and which embodies the generalized social tendencies to which he is biologically wedded, yet at the same time he lives in an associative society which originally was likewise conspicuous for its low degree of internal organization. But suddenly he finds himself faced with a dynamic evolutionary situation in his associative society, far more complex, more highly integrated, and more specialized than the primitive family and associative forms to which, over the millennia of his evolution, he had become biologically adapted. He is as yet but imperfectly adjusted to this unique and dynamic situation. Now his problem is to achieve a difficult and intricate compromise in social living, in which he must successfully harmonize opposite trends and opposing loyalties. In this men and nations are presently confronted with perhaps the most overwhelming challenge ever posed to the social life of the world.

Why should there be this fundamental contradiction in the social structure of man? The possible answers fall roughly into two categories. The first general answer is that, as a biological organism, man has some very remarkable properties, in both his solitary and his social aspects. These are inherent in the youth of his species, in his peculiar genetic make-up, in his innate flexibility, and—above all—in the structure and operation of his brain. A second general answer may be this. Man's biological social organizations, composed of mixtures of the family and associative forms of society, have themselves formed a partnership with, or have become the hosts, so to speak, of another "society" very different in kind. This third form of human "society," which has arisen from the unique quality of the brain of man, we may call human culture.

From the standpoint of human social evolution, possibly the most important characteristic of the "society of culture" is this. In sharp contrast to the biological social form of man, the organization and evolution of human culture present many of the characteristics of a sharply integrated society. Thus we are confronted for the first time in our survey of the social organizations of the world with a situation in which a combination of an associative and a family society has entered into close partnership, as it were, with a dynamically evolving, highly specialized, highly integrated, and dominating "social" structure of culture, which profoundly modifies the associative way.

To appreciate more clearly what this anomalous combination may mean for mankind, in both its advantageous and disadvantageous aspects, it will be profitable to glance for a moment at some of the features of biological man which link him with the rest of the living world and serve as the basis upon which the cultural structure is erected.

CHAPTER 11

The Biology of Man

THE IMPORTANCE of the component of a society in determining the characteristics of that social organization calls for a review of certain characteristics of biological man, both as a solitary and as a social creature. For these have contributed with unusual significance to making his unique societies what they are. A primary query is whether the human individual, in a biological and genetic sense, appears to follow the same laws in respect to his evolution as govern the rest of living matter, or whether man is organically a unique being.

Here the evidence is abundant and clear. All of it indicates that, in the constitution of his protoplasm, in the nature of the cells composing his body, and as a biological entity, there is certainly nothing strikingly unique in man. In physical structure the cells in the body of man are essentially like those of other animals. In such human cells there are separate walls, a well-marked cytoplasmic region, and a definite nucleus. This nucleus contains chromosomes which are demonstrable by the same techniques as obtain for other mammals and appear to be generally similar, being constituted, like those in other organisms, of proteins and nucleic acids. Man conforms to the more usual genetic pattern of higher organisms in having well-marked sexual reproduction, with a double number of chromosomes in the nucleus of each body cell, and a single number in each cell of egg or sperm, which by their union make up the content characteristic of the species. As in other mammals, one pair of the chromosomes in man is specialized to sex determination, and it differs enough in form from its fellows so that it can be distinguished under the microscope.

Functionally, as well as chemically and morphologically, human chromosomes appear to be typical, not only of mammals, but of animals in general. Many identifiable physical and mental characteristics of man are associated with these chromosomes and appear to be the result of the action of specific genes no less than among other organisms. There are well-known recessive and dominant mutations in man that are quite evidently genetically controlled. In the realm of man's physical make-up, these include such features as albinism, red-green color blindness, hemophilia—the often fatal non-coagulation of the blood after a cut—excessive blistering of the feet, sickle-shaped blood corpuscles, and possibly a predisposition to some types of cancer. In the realm of the human mind, it is equally certain that a number of mental and nervous abnormalities are genetically controlled. Further it is becoming ever clearer that the whole mental climate of the individual—his predispositions, his strengths and weaknesses, his genius and his feeble-mindedness—may be importantly influenced by his genetic constitution.

Thus, in his genetic and general biological features man closely resembles other living organisms. Like them he is subject to biological mutation, and his inheritance follows the same general pattern. This being true, it is not surprising that man has not differed radically from other organisms with respect to the biological evolutionary processes which have affected him. Both his individual and his population genetics conform in general to the usual pattern, and the deductions of population genetics should be applicable to the case of man. Some genetic evidence actually exists for this. Such is the population distribution of certain genes for human abnormalities, like that, for instance, of amaurotic idiocy in Sweden, which shows today a peculiar unevenness in distribution, reflecting a tendency in earlier times toward local inbreeding.

known from historical records actually to have been present there.

Thus the evidence concerning the biological constitution of man—evidence which is accumulating at an accelerating rate today—tends to confirm the conjecture that as an organism man should follow the general laws governing the behavior of other organisms. At the same time, however, it is abundantly clear that man is distinguished from all other social organisms by certain very important differences of biological make-up, and consequently of evolutionary pattern.

A striking distinction between man and other social organisms is his extreme evolutionary youth. This biological youth of humanity has important implications. In the first place, it is an eloquent commentary on the comparative stability of the evolution of many other social forms, and of the differing rates at which evolution can proceed among different species at different absolute times. However, this contrast in evolutionary rate is not unprecedented, and although we are far from fully comprehending its underlying causes it is not new in kind. It can be abundantly illustrated elsewhere among living things. Thus the marine brachiopod *Lingula*, which is living today, does not seem to have changed in any essential way from the form of its fossils of Paleozoic time. By contrast, the race of horses has undergone radical changes of form and structure, and probably of habit, since the Miocene, which is roughly one-tenth the time span to the Paleozoic on quite conservative reckoning.

A second and much more important circumstance, however, is unique to human biological evolution. It is clear that, in contrast to the social insects, for instance, the races of modern man never became differentiated in evolution into distinct species. In other words, man has not split into groups which because of intrinsic physiological barriers are no longer able to interbreed. Thus all the living types of men can freely exchange hereditary materials among themselves, provided intermarriage is not precluded by circumstances of geography or culture. It seems probable that in the million or so years of his existence, man has had neither the time nor the opportunity to undergo such physiological differentiation into groups which are mutually exclusive in a genetic sense. This condition of man as a biologically homogeneous species finds no counterpart in any other social or semisocial organism of the world. So far as is known, the tremendous numbers of true species of ants and wasps, bees and termites which have been described are incapable of hybridizing among themselves, or, if capable, hybridize so rarely that the circumstance has little significance in evolution. Thus there is no opportunity for the flow of genes across the separating boundaries and no such opportunity for the recombination and selection of mutations as has apparently been open to the human race throughout the whole course of its evolution. This is an outstanding distinction. It has had some far-ranging effects on the evolution of man.

A third important corollary of the biological youth of humanity is the extent to which individual man has become physiologically adapted to his social life. Impressive in an absolute sense, this adaptation is very slight relative to that of other social organisms. Emphasis has already been laid upon the condition of the individual in those societies which have become thoroughly integrated. Such individuals have commonly become highly specialized to the social milieu and reduced in over-all capacity—deindividualized, as it were. In effect, they have become worker bees or warrior ants or the irreversibly adapted soldiers of a termite colony.

In a biological sense man has gone but a very short distance down this road. Yet he may not have wholly escaped it. There is some evidence that the socialization of man has made itself felt in an incipient way in the physiological structure or functions of the commoner types in modern human populations, though the mark which it has left has been light indeed in comparison with many other social creatures. For instance, it seems likely that in a physical sense many modern men are somewhat modified— possibly even somewhat "infantilized"—versions of pre-Chellean man in so far as the physique of the latter can be visualized. Undoubtedly a typical modern adult in certain aspects presents an underdeveloped or highly modified physical appearance in contrast to corresponding aspects of the great apes.

The recollection that an arresting of development distinguishes the soldier termite from the more socially generalized queen or male, and that a still further degree of arrest, in turn, characterizes the worker, is of interest here. All the non-reproductive castes of the social insects are of course physiologically arrested and highly modified types in which the development, if it parallels that of modern man at all, has gone much further, is much more conspicuous, and has been brought about by different selectional processes. Yet the urban man of today is notoriously deficient in the use, if not in the innate quality, of his senses compared with many of his less socialized contemporaries, such as the native Australian or the Mongol of northern steppes, and his integrative centers are on the whole probably more active.

This same condition is characteristic of the social insects, even in a physiological sense. Thus the brain of the socially practically undeveloped male of the ant *Lasius*, for example, consists of a small central mass of nervous tissues connected with relatively immense nerve trunks which serve the huge compound eyes, the antennae, and the other organs of perception. These tracts have a major function to fulfill, for the simple reproductive pattern which dominates the life of this insect requires good senses but no great powers of integration. By way of contrast, in the worker *Lasius* the sensory tracts occupy a much smaller proportion of the total brain mass, which is dominated instead by centers which appear to be largely integrative and co-ordinative in function. It may well be that the complicated psychic powers of the worker *Lasius*, compared to the male, are correlated with these structural changes in much the same way as the heightened mental processes of modern man are believed to be correlated with the relatively recent and conspicuous development of the human forebrain.

This development and modification of the brain occurs on

very different planes in men and in the social insects. But the general trend is similar, and it may well be of very great significance with respect to social life as a whole. In the more primitive social phases among both man and the social invertebrates, the individual is necessarily in general a much more "externalized" creature than his more socially specialized descendant. At a later stage of evolution a curious "internalization" takes place in both men and invertebrates. Conditions arising within the individual or within the social fabric come to be much more important in determining the course of social evolution than the mere environment outside the communal sphere, which has long since been satisfactorily adjusted.

The young queen of the primitive ant and the member of a New Guinea tribe are alike much more "externalized" individuals, necessarily far more seriously concerned with their inanimate environment, than the queen of a higher ant at the center of her colony or the businessman of a modern great city, whose primary absorption must be with stimuli arising within the social milieu. This tendency to "internalization" of the individual with absorption into a social fabric can often be seen recapitulated within the life span of a single organism. Thus the initially highly "externalized" and feverishly active young queen of the slave-making ant *Polyergus*, which, if she is to live and reproduce, must fly and mate and then as a solitary individual overpower a young community of her slave species, becomes metamorphosed into the sedentary and "internalized" old queen of the successful nest, concerned only with life within the colony which she has created.

This tendency toward internalization is apparently common to all social creatures. It deserves emphasizing, for it reaches an unprecedented climax in human social evolution, where it becomes a mainspring of cultural development in the very widest sense. It is, of course, another aspect of a very general property of living things—the property of life, as it evolves, to become a most potent influence in directing the further evolutionary course of the life which follows it. It also represents an incipient stage of the trend of the individual toward dependence upon its social milieu which is carried to its greatest height in the thoroughly integrated society.

What is most important to notice, however, is that the biological modification of the human individual which appears to have taken place in response to social development has progressed but a relatively short distance. There is little doubt that man in his brief social experience has been subjected to evolutionary influences similar to those affecting other communal organisms. However, while some evidence of incipient biological specialization of the human individual to the social way can be detected, nowhere in the race of man can one find indication of any such physiological specialization of the individual to particular functions within the society as distinguishes the members of ant or termite or other biologically integrated associations. On the contrary, human evolution seems rather to have progressed in the opposite direction— toward the production of an immensely varied, enormously plastic and adaptable organism.

There is another feature in which man as a biological organism differs so greatly in degree from the rest of the social world as almost to differ in kind. This is in the intimate nature and the quality of function of the human brain. This feature, though often taken for granted, has had consequences of tremendous importance for human social evolution.

Despite the remarkable functioning of its more specialized parts, the human brain is by no means entirely unique. In its more generalized reaches it operates very much according to the usual pattern of the central nervous system of mammals and probably differs much less in structure from the brain of a dog than the latter does from the cephalic ganglia of an ant. But from recent extensive work in comparative psychology it is clear that there is a profound functional gulf between the vertebrate and the invertebrate brain, and in particular between the brain types of the higher mammals, including man, on the one hand and the higher social insects on the other.

These researches give more exact expression to long-current common knowledge that whereas in social living individual men are predominantly motivated by the sort of plastic mental processes which are vaguely termed intellect, the social invertebrates are dominated primarily by those much more fixed nervous patterns which, again in a very imprecise way, are called instincts. Each of these different modes of mental behavior is highly adaptive and effective. Each is of much importance in determining the mechanics of operation of its particular kind of resultant society. But they differ widely in many ways.

Both mammals and ants have excellent memories. Both are capable of fairly rapid associative learning in comparatively simple situations. Ants sometimes exhibit the most remarkable powers of retention of the solutions of maze problems once these are thoroughly fixed in their minds. In this respect, ants may quite equal the performance of rats in certain situations. But if the problem is suddenly changed or a new difficulty is interposed, the score will be abruptly and radically altered in favor of the mammal. If any considerable relation exists between the old and the new problem, the solution which the rat has already learned may aid it in meeting the new challenge. But the solution which the ant has already fixed in mind may become a dangerous liability to it in mastering the new situation unless the two are very specifically related in particular ways. This implies that the rodent brain has considerable capacity for relating an old solution to a new one and combining them to master a new problem. But such an analysis and recombination of solutions, except in very elementary situations, is well beyond the scope of the brain of the ant.

The invertebrate brain is peculiarly adept at building up and retaining rather complex behavior patterns by successive accretion. But once the slate is filled, it cannot be easily erased, nor can the phrases of the writing on it be easily segregated or rearranged.

Synthesis there is, but it is largely of an elementary, additive kind. There is remarkably little analysis. Thus knowledge, which is of such importance to a rat, a dog, or a man, may become a serious liability to an ant.

However, this does not mean that a social invertebrate is incapable of learning. Quite the contrary. There is abundant evidence that young social insects in nature—the young worker bee making her first flight, the fresh-hatched army ant participating in her first raid—do learn considerably from experience, and later put this learning to good use. But the situation in which the knowledge has been gained and to which it applies must remain rather constant. For, whatever the requirements of the environment, once the information gained is absorbed, it can be little modified. It is as though the invertebrate mind functioned like a shallow vessel which, once filled, cannot be emptied. By contrast, the vertebrate mind is a deeper pitcher. It may be partially emptied many times, and as often refilled with liquids of another dye. As the mammalian mind grows older, it grows wiser. Faced with a rapidly changing environment, the invertebrate mind merely grows less well adapted and more thoroughly confused.

This difference between the mammalian and the invertebrate mind may be intimately linked to the contrast between the predominant role of instinct in the social lives of the invertebrates and the conspicuous role of plastic intellect among the mammals. This in turn may be related in part to the much greater store of neural elements in the brains of mammals—a store to which the insects, because of their relatively minute size, can never attain. The fact that the learning powers of the invertebrates are largely restricted to the early days of adult existence, coupled with the fact that the impressions which they then receive and collate are for the most part retained in unmodified form, must severely limit their capacity of absorbing and reacting to new and complicated situations. Thus it is almost inconceivable that the delicately adjusted individual functions and the store of individual wisdom involved in the maintenance of such an intricate social structure as the ant or bee colony could be maintained or accumulated unless another psychic reservoir were available.

This reservoir is evidently provided by the remarkable instinct endowment of the higher insects—by that store of action patterns, perhaps even of channels of "thought," which are as much characteristic of the germ plasm of the particular species exhibiting them as the color of its eyes. The mechanics by which such complex instinct patterns can be inherited and reproduced year after year without training or previous individual experience are unknown. Yet it is clear beyond all doubt that this does happen, and perhaps as a phenomenon it is no more remarkable than that the color of the hair of men should be similarly transmitted by heredity.

Because these instinct patterns abound among the social insects and show an exquisite adjustment to the communal way of life, it is not to be supposed that they are absent from the mental equipment of mammals, including man. In varying degrees, they are innate properties of all warm-blooded creatures, and they play an important role in human social existence. They clearly dominate such elemental biological drives as those of nourishment and reproduction, in mankind no less than elsewhere. Moreover, a whole range of biologically inherited human aptitudes may make themselves felt in a wider and more subtle sphere of social activity.

In the present state of our knowledge, this vast subject of the social role of human instinct-patterns can only be a subject of conjecture. Yet, suggestive evidence on this score does appear from time to time, and it is well not to lose sight of the possibility that our instinct endowment may be more important than we usually think. For instance, it is often a cause of wonder that various features of the cultures of peoples remote from one another in space and time may yet show astonishing similarities. Sometimes it seems most probable that similar factors in the respective environments, evoking parallel responses, are the causes of this similarity. Sometimes ancient connections and exchanges of culture can be traced. But some situations elude both of these explanations.

An interesting example is the oft-remarked general similarity between much of the design art of the pre-Incaic Nazca and Chimu peoples of western South America and of the Old and New Empires of the Mayas on the one hand, and that of northern China and Mongolia on the other. It would be a bold archeologist or historian who would attempt to adduce a significant similarity of environment between the homelands of these culture complexes of the New and Old Worlds to account for their undoubted resemblances. It is quite possible that there was enough direct cultural connection between them to account fully for their parallel development. On the other hand, it seems credible that all these peoples originally radiated from a common parental stock at a remote period—quite possibly at a time when that stock had not developed pottery, let alone conceived the art forms with which it was later to be decorated. In such case the similarities of culture which later appeared among these distant folk might be conceived to have been influenced by complex but common genetic predispositions. Thus the resultant art forms may possibly have had much the same "genetic" basis as the similarity of the paper nests built by the yellow jacket—*Vespula sylvestris*—in England with that of its counterpart *Vespula maculata* in America.

Further speculations of this sort are tempting. But they would be idle. This illustration merely emphasizes the fact that inherited predispositions to behavior patterns must not be considered negligible in the social life of man, any more than the intellectual function of learning should be viewed as wholly absent from the societies of insects. Indeed, as has recently been emphasized, the sharp distinctions often drawn between instinct and intelligence are probably misleading. They imply a difference in kind in mental functioning whereas, in all probability, what exists is but a difference in degree. It is not possible to draw a sharp dividing line. But there is undeniably a profound contrast between the invertebrates and the mammals in the complexity of the relationships which can be perceived and the situations to which adaptive behavior can be adjusted. This difference is so great as to constitute a very real and important distinction.

If the mammalian brain, considered generally as including the cerebrum of man, thus exhibits a far greater degree of plasticity in its normal functioning than the intellect of the social insect, so likewise the human brain is quite unique even in the mammalian class in another capacity. This characteristic, which has been of tremendous significance in human social development, is the power of abstract ideation. There is no reliable evidence that any of the invertebrates are capable of this kind of thinking, in which a symbol is manipulated as the substitute for an abstract idea. There is some evidence that a few of the higher mammals can do this to a slight extent, though one suspects that this ability may have been acquired by the particular animal through association with the human experimenter himself. In any event, so far as is known, this remarkable capacity, upon which man relies very greatly, is of little service to any other social organism of the world. This factor has made possible the whole range of human culture, extending into all the subtle and manifold manifestations of our modern civilization, including its most noble expressions in the sphere of the spirit—the wealth of symbolism, the etherealization and internalization of cultures, and, noblest of all, the evolution of the great religions.

So far as their simple mechanics are concerned, many of the manifestations of such culture are of course not unique to the human race. Speech is mechanically only an elaborated use of call systems similar to those of many species of ants, bees, termites, and semisocial vertebrates, not to mention many essentially solitary forms using similar devices. Writing is mechanically but an elaborated pattern of the marking by which the little parasite *Telenomus* designates the butterfly egg that she has parasitized, warning later comers away. The power of using tools is an elaborated expression of the technique of the solitary wasp *Ammophila*, many females of which are adepts at tamping the scattered earth about their burrows with pebbles, or of the Galápagos woodpecker finch *Camarhynchus,* which employs cactus spines in probing for wood-dwelling insects. Neither is the capacity to build large structures for communal use peculiar to man. Witness the nests of ants and wasps, the hives of bees, and the communal dwellings of the sociable weaver birds.

But these are merely mechanics. It is the extreme powers of ideation, the rapid powers of imitation, the heightened capacities for analysis, the relatively immense capabilities of speedy recombination of elements of thinking and action, which have brought the development of human culture to such intricacy and have given it such an important significance in human social evolution. So great is this importance that it is in man alone that there must be distinguished two separate, though closely interlinked, modes of evolution—the biological and the cultural.

There is one more significant aspect in which the biological evolution of man has differed from that of all other social creatures. This is the retention of the ability of the human race to interbreed throughout its entire range, which has already been briefly alluded to. In this sense the whole complex of humanity throughout the world has remained a single species.

Little enough is known about the early phases of man's social history, and knowledge of his beginnings as a biological organism is fragmentary indeed. Nevertheless, all that is known and all that can be conjectured points to the conclusion that primitive men lived in relatively isolated small tribal groups that for many generations must have been rather closely wedded to definite territorial areas which formed reserved hunting grounds, even as the few primitive Australoids that survive today tend to cling to the particular restricted desert or coastal areas that have supported their ancestors for untold generations. Further, it seems unlikely that ancient man had much intercourse with other tribes at any great distance—tribes which he would ordinarily regard as hostile. To be sure, judging by the behavior of many contemporary primitive peoples, he may have intermarried with his immediate neighbors, even if he considered them dangerous enemies. But it is unlikely that his social contacts with neighboring groups ever went much farther afield than this, save through the medium of trading. Certainly the social contacts of any single human group in the very early era must have been limited compared with the number of peoples potentially available for such contacts over the surface of the earth. Thus it seems probable that each tribal entity of very early humans formed a relatively small interbreeding population that was largely isolated genetically.

Now the course of evolution and of natural selection in a small and isolated interbreeding population differs from that in a large cosmopolitan group in significant ways. Since there can be little or no flow of genes across the boundaries separating such populations of the same species, they soon tend to diverge from one another. Each group rapidly becomes more perfectly adapted to the particular detailed features of the environment which it occupies. Eventually groups which were originally homogeneous become sharply distinguished in many characteristics.

This selective divergence among isolated populations of the same species leads to the establishment of a great variety of characteristics which are highly adaptive to particular environments. At the same time recessive lethal mutations tend to be eliminated from the collective germ plasm of small isolated populations at a higher rate than occurs in larger groups, as has been discussed at an earlier point in this book.

In their relatively atomistic isolation, the human groups scattered over the earth must early have developed and fixed a great number of variant qualities. A large proportion of these characteristics were probably adaptive to some perhaps very subtle feature of the particular environment in which each tribal entity had dwelt. Some qualities, perhaps, had no strikingly positive value in a particular environment, but might acquire such a meaning amid different surroundings. While all these variant traits may have been either uniquely beneficial or largely of indifferent

value, few were seriously deleterious. For such deleterious qualities would long have been under an evolutionary pressure leading
to their elimination. Indeed, the germ plasm of the human race
as a whole must have been unusually thoroughly cleansed of these
deleterious mutations during the early period of atomistic isolation.

Thus at the close of the very earliest period of its social development it may be supposed that the human race was for the most
part composed of small groups which for many generations had
not mixed with their neighbors to any considerable extent. It
was unusually free of lethal mutations and was possessed of a large
store of divergent characteristics, some of which had been proved
of advantage in evolution while others remained to be tested in
new environments. In this respect ancient man cannot have
differed greatly from modern ants. They also are split into a very
great number of relatively small, but in this case permanently
isolated, populations (species, in fact), separated for many generations.

The next step, however, must have had momentous consequences. Man learned and dared to travel far afield in great numbers. The pre-Dravidian folk poured into India, perhaps through
the northern passes, and on into Ceylon, the East Indies, and Australia. The Melanesians began their island-hopping exploits, until
they came to tenant a large proportion of the islands of the southern seas. Following them, the more modern Polynesians achieved
still greater exploits of island conquest. The men of Europe invaded the New World. In Europe itself feudal estates dissolved,
mingling populations of serfs hitherto long isolated. Cities were
formed from villages, and nations from city-states. Finally North
America became a racial and a cultural melting pot, and within its
great metropolitan centers members of every race and nation of
the world commingled.

Now this sort of geographic blending of previously isolated
social groups is by no means peculiar to man. Such ants as *Pheidole
megacephala* and *Iridomyrmex humilis* have achieved worldwide

distribution in historical times, crossing the territories of other species and even exterminating them within their own homelands. It is quite likely that other species of aggressive social organisms have attained worldwide distribution through the ages of evolution. What is unique in the human case, and what lends poignant significance to the whole human situation, is that the races of men that thus infringed upon one another's territory were *still capable of interbreeding* and of merging once again the streams of inheritance that had so long flowed in separate channels. They had not become separate species.

This fusion must have begun in very ancient times. It is attested by a series of recent remarkable archeological discoveries at Mount Carmel in Palestine. A great collection of human bones was found, indicating that the site had long been occupied by successive prehistoric encampments. The amazing thing about these intermingled skeletal fragments is that some of them are almost purely Neanderthaloid in character while others are essentially modern in type. Still others exhibit a complex commingling of traits of the two races. This situation can be convincingly explained as the result of an interbreeding of these originally distinct groups.[1]

It seems possible that Mount Carmel lay near the boundaries of the territories of two peoples, one Neanderthal and the other modern in character, or else that a settlement of one race was overrun by members of the other and intermarriage took place as in countless instances in later ages. Such a process of widening and deepening the genetic stream of man has certainly been going forward actively and continuously into modern times. Thus it is interesting to notice that in Prussia the frequency of cousin marriages, which in the years 1875–1880 was 0.71 per cent, dropped in the period 1921–1926 to 0.20 per cent, and in Bavaria it decreased from 0.87 per cent in 1876–1880 to 0.20 per cent in 1926–1933.[2]

[1] Th. Dobzhansky, "On Species and Races of Living and Fossil Man," *Am. J. Phys. Anthrop.*, N.S., V. 2, No. 3, September, 1944.

[2] Th. Dobzhansky, *Genetics and the Origin of Species.* New York, Columbia University Press, 1941.

Such has been the decrease of inbreeding and the increase of out-crossing in the human race even within modern times.

In this great mingling and fusion which today proceeds with vastly intensified dynamism, man has finally drawn upon a priceless genetic heritage. Unlike all other social animals of the world, his isolation had been geographic only. And so he brought to this genetic melting pot the whole vast selection of characters that had been fixed within the various isolated social groups during the primitive ages. Many of these characters, originally useless, undoubtedly proved to have an unsuspected value in new settings. Others, which had originally been useful, were doubtless reduced to impotence. Still others were undoubtedly harmful. But the whole content of this rich range of genetically fixed potentialities was now subjected to the process of natural selection within this new and vastly larger interbreeding population. And to this store of characteristics was added another, of extreme importance to man throughout his whole history. For man has been peculiar among biological organisms in that, throughout his evolution, great emphasis has been laid on the capacity for *generalized, adaptive behavior* rather than upon rigid patterns highly perfected for certain set situations. So man probably came upon the threshold of his domination of the world with his germ plasm unusually free of genetic lethals, and with an immense variety of inherited characteristics, among which an evolutionary selection *among individuals* could be made for the most effective in any particular environment which he might choose. Best of all, he possessed a peculiar capacity for flexible adaptive behavior. In a purely biological sense, what richer endowment could any creature ask?

These, then, are some of the ways in which the biological constitution of individual man, and the biological character of his social evolution, on the one hand resemble, and on the other differ from, the general biological pattern of other social life in nature. The conclusion is inescapable that in the fundamental factors of biological constitution and evolution, the condition of man is essentially that of the rest of the organic world. In his genetics, and in the play between his hereditary constitution and the forces of selection and adaptation, man is similar to other social animals, and in its broadest aspects the course of his rise and development has been as theirs. But there are important differences which are peculiar to man, and these have had the most profound consequences in molding the growth and the structure of his societies.

As a species, he is biologically very youthful, and he has ranged widely over the earth. These conditions are coupled with others of profoundly important implications. One of these is that the various races of man have never lost the ability to interbreed. Again, while it is true that individual man shows some physiological specialization to the general social mode of life, which is reflected in a number of characteristics of his body and mind, he shows essentially no physical differentiation of the sort which has given rise to the castes of the social insects, with their predetermined and unalterable functions in the community. Thus, on a biological plane, human society exhibits a very low degree of internal specialization as compared with that of the higher social insects.

Again, the youth of man, when combined with his early social history in isolated groups and the later fusion of these to form larger aggregates in which all the members were still capable of interbreeding, has given the human race immense biological advantages over all other social creatures of the world. Man has long been evolving toward plasticity, adaptability, and flexibility in both physique and behavior. Finally the structure of the mammalian brain—in particular the peculiar structure and function of the human mind—has been an immensely important factor in molding human social evolution and in distinguishing it from that of all other social creatures. Because of these mental qualities, the processes of intellect discharge many of the social functions served by instinct among the invertebrates. Because of them too, abstract ideation has become important for man. It has made possible a new kind of social evolution, which is rooted in the processes and characteristics of the human biological society but which must be considered quite distinct from it and sometimes opposed to it. The result is a culture complex which, in contrast to the biological aspects of human social living, in many respects bears strange resemblances to an integrated animal society.

CHAPTER 12

The Society of Human Culture

MAN DOES not live by bread alone.

Variously phrased by philosopher, poet, and priest, how constantly has this thought been reiterated down the ages! How poignant is the testimony it offers that if we would truly understand the social life of man, we must look far beyond its biological aspects to those mental and spiritual elements which are of controlling importance within it!

The essence of all the profound but ill-defined visions of the higher nature of human civilization which have so often occurred to thoughtful men lies deep within this duality of its nature—a duality which springs primarily from the extraordinary quality of the human mind. There is the sharpest possible contrast between the purely biological life of man and his life as a thinking and exquisitely sentient being. As a biological organism, he shows close relationships in structure and behavior with the rest of the living world. The structure of his protoplasm is as theirs, his chromosomes and genes behave like those of other higher multicellular organisms, and the mechanisms of his inheritance are Mendelian. Even his nervous system shows a close kinship with those of other vertebrates, and his mind, in the fundamental aspects of its structure, is akin to theirs. But in its extraordinary powers of ideation and abstract thinking, in its powers of analysis and synthesis, the human mind is so different in degree from the typical vertebrate brain as almost to differ in kind.

200

This then, is the starting-point of the culture society—the extraordinary complex of ideas which inhabit the brain of an individual man and their consequences. This complex may, without too much fancifulness, be regarded as being in itself a living, changing adaptive "organism," with an independent existence and evolution of its own. It is incorporeal, to be sure, but many of its consequences can be vividly seen and felt, and they are of vital importance. Inhabiting the body of a man and vitally influencing many of his activities, made possible by the physical structure of his brain, it is somewhat like a parasite or symbiont, being dependent upon and closely linked to his physical organization, but nonetheless dominating that physical organization and shaping its course to an extraordinary degree. Thus the modern civilized individual may be regarded as not one, but two, organisms which are interdependent and in the closest partnership. They function in closely co-operative ways, yet often also in ways which are remarkably divergent.

Now this complex of ideas and their consequences in an individual man can be looked on as one component of a social entity. It easily aggregates with the idea-complexes of other men to form "societies," so to speak, which in some ways resemble but in others radically differ from human biological societies. These strange societies taken as a whole embody human culture, including the whole complex of human thought and its consequent action, ranging from the invention of the first stone tool to our modern industrial technology, from the first fragment of articulate speech to the highest flights of oratory, from the first intentional planting of a seed by a savage hesitating on the brink of the agricultural age to mechanized agriculture itself.

The "society" of human culture, like the "organism" of individual human thought, carries on an independent evolution of its own. Like a true living society, it is subject to "mutations," represented in this case by the origination of new ideas. It is subject to definite rules of inheritance and selection, represented by the propagation of new ideas from one group to another, and the competition between ideas for usefulness in survival. In all these fundamental aspects, this so-called society of human culture bears a close functional similarity to other societies. Yet in these mechanisms of mutation, inheritance, and selection, the culture society differs radically from societies elsewhere in the living world. These differences are extraordinarily important in setting the evolution of culture sharply apart from biological evolution in its intense dynamism and in conferring upon it some fundamentally novel features.

The "society" of human culture, like the "organism" represented by the complex of ideas of an individual brain, may be compared to a symbiont or parasite. Its partner or host is human society in its biological aspect. Together, these two societies make up the structure of human civilization. Thus human civilization may be fancifully regarded as the remote analogue of a lichen, composed on the one hand of a fungus—the human biological society—which gives it structure, texture, and stability, and on the other of an alga—the society of human culture—which gives it color, energizes it, and makes possible its dynamic activities.

As with the lichen, the human civilization which arises from this symbiosis is precisely like neither of its components. It is much more than a combination of the two, having an emergent personality of its own. Like the lichen, too, it has great advantages and strengths which result from a harmonious combination of the mutually advantageous and reinforcing qualities of its components. But it differs from the lichen in that it suffers severely when these qualities of its partners clash bitterly, as they often do. It is from these deep-seated disharmonies between biological man and the kind of society that he builds and is adapted to, and between the nature of the "organism" of culture and the kind of culture society which it tends to evolve that many of the difficulties, the inconsistencies, and the deep-seated troubles of higher civilizations have sprung throughout recorded history. It is from them, perhaps, that the most fundamental problems in our contemporary civilization arise.

These are the postulates in which the analogy of the culture society is rooted. This strictly hypothetical analogy, when handled with abundant caution, can be both illuminating and useful. Its net consequence is that the complex of ideas generated by a human brain may be regarded as an "organism" with definite evolutionary potentialities; that it is a social organism, making up the societies which we call human culture, and that these societies, existing in the closest partnership with human biological society—family and associative—constitute human civilization. Moreover, the society that is human culture is governed in evolution by the same broad principles which govern the growth and structure of other societies. It shows the same trends to complexity, to specialization, to integration that they do. But it also exhibits many important differences, and it does not follow that the society of human culture has always evolved in the same direction, or at the same rate, as the societies of biological man with which it is so closely linked.

It is well to reiterate that all the analogies which have been suggested must be considered as purely functional similitudes if one is not to be led astray by superficial resemblances between different phenomena. Functional similarities, however, may have great value and significance here as elsewhere. For evolution, progress, and change are the matters of prime interest here, and the aim is to deduce something of the probable evolutionary course of human civilization from the biological evolutionary roads already discussed. This approach is well known to professional psychologists.[1]

Bearing this caution in mind, two significant characteristics of the human culture society, of fundamental importance in determining the nature of human civilization as a whole, demand consideration and illustration. The first is that in the very basis of its organization and its evolution this culture society is an *integrated*

[1] It is set forth with unusual cogency in the recent Harvard Report "The Place of Psychology in the Ideal University," (*Report of the University to Advise on the Future of Psychology at Harvard, Harvard University Press,* 1947, pp. 6–7).

social form. As such it is perhaps more comparable to the societies of higher social insects than to the primarily associative biological social form of man. Certainly it stands in the sharpest possible contrast to the biological societies of prehistoric man as we know them, to which man as an organism is still thoroughly adapted, even today.

There is good evidence that these latter societies regularly consisted of loosely integrated family-type structures of rather few individuals welded into and existing in close combination with even more loosely integrated associative forms resulting from the natural gregariousness of men.

The second important characteristic of the "society" of human culture follows from the first. It has been shown that family-type and associative societies are by their very nature compatible, and mixtures of them are widespread among other social creatures. It is not surprising, therefore, that such a combination is to be found in primitive human societies, and probably it was inherently practical throughout the social evolution of man. But it has already been emphasized that the integrated form of social living is basically incompatible with either family or associative societies, by virtue of important and fundamental differences of structure between them and of the divergent courses which they tend to follow in evolution. Consistent with this surmise, combinations of these societies are not ordinarily found in nature. In human civilization alone that powerfully integrated and recently evolved "society" that is human culture exists in close if uneasy partnership with the ancient biological family and associative forms of social living which were native to ancient man, and to which modern man is still irrevocably committed. What is even more remarkable, while the integrated culture society partly dominates both of the others, it also reinforces and secures them.

But why consider the human culture society to be the analogue of the integrated rather than the associative biological form? There are several reasons. It will be recalled that one of the important characteristics distinguishing biologically integrated societies is the fact that all of their members are closely related genetically, that all of them bear essentially similar gene complexes in their chromosomes, and that a mutation which drives one member in the direction of social specialization and dependence, is likely eventually to be shared by other members of the community. The result is a stabilization and closer knitting of the social structure.

Now ideas—the "genes" of the cultural society—do not need to be biologically inherited in order to be transmitted throughout the civilization which they affect. In the cultural realm this effect is achieved by imitation and the processes of learning. In consequence, all the components of a culture society are functionally as closely related as though they were genetic kin. If a "mutation" in the form of a new idea becomes established, it will affect them quite as universally as would a genic mutation in the closely related kin of a biological integrated society. Thus the genetic barrier which helps to prevent an associative society from behaving like an integrated one is completely removed in the society that is human culture. It is left free to pursue the evolutionary road of the integrated social form if other influences impel it along this path. And such compelling forces are not wanting.

The relative permanence of the culture society does much to ensure that it shall behave like an integrated social structure. It is probably safe to say that, with very few exceptions, from the most primitive aboriginal to the most sophisticated urbanite, all human beings are born into a specific culture. They live out their existences in this environment, adding to it or otherwise modifying it, much as an ant lives out its span in the milieu of its colony and its nest. Finally they die within this same protecting sphere, never in their whole lives having been called upon to exist entirely outside it as autonomous and cultureless biological organisms. There is every opportunity for the human individual in his mental life to become as highly specialized to the environment provided by his culture and as dependent upon it as is the worker bee in relation to its hive. The truth of this is readily apparent from one historical example of a rare exception to this rule.

The great Linnaeus, father of modern systems of classification of plants and animals, was so convinced that the wild waif-children who were occasionally captured in the Europe of his time were unlike the ordinary run of human beings that he actually classified them as a different species—*Homo ferus*. Yet actually they were only unfortunates who had been abandoned in infancy and yet had managed to survive and to grow outside the culture to which they properly belonged, though only as mentally malformed individuals who were culturally almost unrecognizable. How far such mental specialization of the individual to his culture society has gone, and how markedly the culture society takes on the typical aspect of an integrated organization in this regard, is brought vividly home when one reflects on how difficult it is to accept a radical change in one's cultural milieu when it concerns elements which are regarded as vital. Every great war has demonstrated that there are many millions of human beings who would prefer death to a compulsory shift of this sort.

The structure of culture suggests the integrated society in yet another way. This is the manner in which new ideas, new concepts, are selected, adopted, and made to survive in the course of cultural evolution. Within a particular culture complex, such ideas are selected and find acceptance, not wholly upon their absolute merits, but upon their merit, appropriateness, and relevance *within that particular cultural structure*. This is much more nearly analogous to the sort of intercommunal selection for *social* fitness which characterizes the evolution of the integrated society and leads to the predominance of specialized, socially dependent members within it than it is to the intracommunal selection so typical of family or associative groups. What is perhaps more significant, within groups of men organized to develop and exploit elements of culture, such as a profession or an industrial enterprise, selection of the members tends to be made very largely on the basis of cultural attributes especially suitable to that particular group. The selection, therefore, is made on an intercommunal rather than an intracommunal basis, in important part. That this type of selection may lead to high mental specialization and social dependence of the individual caught up in such a situation, no less than it leads to high physical specialization and social dependence in the worker of the ant community, needs no emphasis. Here it is that one of the major conflicts arises between the evolutionary courses of biological man and of his culture.

These are some of the factors in the culture "society" which seem analogous to certain characteristics of integrated societies in the biological realm. Now if the human cultural "society" thus exhibits many of the structural qualities of an integrated social form, it follows that it should have shown trends to increasing complexity and integration in evolution, like integrated societies elsewhere. Moreover, like them, human culture in any age should consistently make more complex the environment against and in which later culture must evolve, thus accelerating the trend to complexity. The correctness of both these assumptions is observationally confirmed in many aspects of human cultural evolution, and especially by the vast increase in the dynamism of such evolution in recent times. This increase is tremendous. It will be recalled that by far the largest part of the cultural evolution of man has taken place in the last ten thousand of the million or so years of his biological existence.

The culture "society" exhibits other evolutionary trends typical of integrated biological societies, such as the development of polarity and leadership, simplification and specialization under particular conditions, and the capacity to follow highly integrated functional patterns, such as those involved in modern warfare. Furthermore, it is liable to various internal ills typical of the integrated society, such as may be inherent in parasitism and in slavery. Many of the comparisons which have been tentatively drawn in earlier pages between elements of integrated biological societies on the one hand and human civilization on the other have pointed, albeit not explicitly, to this conjecture.

Finally, if the human culture "society" is an integrated one, it should exhibit many of the elements making for cohesiveness. It should show strong internal binding ties analogous to the binding fibers in the Portuguese man-of-war and the institution of trophallaxis among the social insects. Such binding ties are abundant and conspicuous in the modern culture "society." Speech and the modern communication system, as well as primitive barter and modern trade and economics, are but a few of them.

The linchpin joining the biological social organization and man's culture society in that intimate union called civilization is the human mind. Its extraordinary powers of generating and handling and recombining ideas are basic to the culture society. Indeed, the integrative trend in the culture society may well be in large part a reflection of the integrative properties of the human mind. Fascinating evidence for this exists in recent studies of the structure and functioning of the mind in evolution.

The history of evolution of the vertebrate brain has been largely one of an increasing power to discover more and more refined elements in living situations and to organize them upon successively wider and higher planes. The chimpanzee can discover elements in problem situations which never become apparent to the spider monkey. Moreover, it can relate them in useful channels that are forever closed to its more lowly-evolved kin. Both are keenly aware of elements and organizational relationships which must remain forever unperceived by a bird such as the tern. It is a striking reflection that the only correlation between brain structure and the advancement of behavioral pattern among vertebrate animals which has been found to be consistently valid is that of the ratio of the weight of the brain to the total weight of the body. The only consistently relevant brain factor determining the extent and character of adaptive behavior in vertebrates so far found, therefore, seems to be how much excess brain tissue is available beyond the demands of motor and bodily functions and freed to discover new relationships and to combine and recombine them. This all points strongly to the fact that the vertebrate mind, in both its structural and functional aspects, has followed the typical paths of complexity and integration in the course of its evolution.

It is important to inquire whether the human mind has continued to evolve in this same general pattern, though on a loftier plane of complexity and integration. The structural evidence for this, while somewhat meager, is generally confirmatory. The evidence seems good that, in the course of the evolution of men taken over its wide sweeps, the ratio of brain weight to body weight has tended to increase. Thus proportionately more and more cellular elements may have become available for the perception and the organization of more esoteric relationships, extrinsic to immediate needs. Indeed, it is amusing to reflect that if a mutation in the human species should occur so that *one more generation* of primordial brain cells should become available in the course of embryonic development than is now the case, the result might well be a race of incomparable geniuses.

These are some of the more abstract reasons why the society of human culture may be regarded as being of the integrated type. Now how is it possible for this integrated society to exist in close conjunction with the associative portion of human biological society represented by the crowd or the tribe, when everywhere else in nature these two kinds of society are wholly incompatible? The explanation of this extraordinary situation may lie in the same factor which enables the culture society itself to behave like an integrated organization, and makes possible its intense dynamism. This crucial factor is the manner of the "inheritance" of its "genes" —human ideas—and the manner of their propagation throughout the social structure.

The means by which the idea-mutations of the culture society are propagated throughout the social structure are largely independent of the relatively slow and restricted processes of ordinary biological inheritance. This fact is self-evident, but is nonetheless profoundly significant. A hypothetical illustration will not be amiss. Compare a cultural innovation in the history of an imaginary people with a germinal mutation affecting the instinct endowment and the behavior pattern of a social insect. Each of these circumstances introduces a novel, a contributory, and a transmissible element into the social structure. But the rates at which these innovations can be propagated through the society and the extent of their immediate dissemination will be vastly different.

The social insects, with their limited powers of learning, will be able to transmit very few if any of such innovations by the process of imitation, even within the colony where they occurred. Transmission from colony to colony in this fashion will be practically ruled out in those forms where a marked antipathy normally exists between communities even of the same species, offering negligible opportunities for the commingling of different communities. Newly arisen modifications of instinct patterns in ants, for these reasons among other important ones, must therefore rely on the conventional mechanisms of inheritance for their transmission. And these mechanisms are so involved and hazardous that the chances that such mutations will eventually become established must be very low.

Suppose, for example, that such a mutation has occurred in a species of ant which forms very populous communities, like one of the fungus growers. In such colonies there may be as many as thirty thousand workers compared with a few hundred, at most, of young queens. One must suppose that such a mutation in instinct-pattern is as likely to arise in one of the young workers as it is in a young queen. Thus such a mutation—rare in any case—has but a small chance of appearing in a queen. Yet only if it appears in such a potentially reproductive individual will it have any great likelihood of being fixed in the germ plasm.

As if this hazard to the spread of the mutation were not enough, there is an even greater one. From what is known of the evolution of populations of such solitary insects as the fruit fly, it appears likely that a large proportion of natural mutations are or ultimately become recessive. Therefore, even if the original instinct-mutation should have occurred in a young queen, it would probably not find immediate expression in the colonial economy of the next generation. If its inheritance were typical it could not find expression until enough generations had passed so that some daughter queen carrying this recessive mutation should mate with some male also carrying it, in which case one-fourth of her potential queen-daughters would presumably express the character, and possibly transmit it to the workers of their communities. But even then, when the mutation had finally received some general expression, it seems clear from studies of fruit-fly genetics that, unless it conferred a very decided selective advantage on the community which carried it, it would never become very common in the homozygous form. With such tremendous difficulties to overcome, it is remarkable that social instincts involving such elaborate behavior patterns as those required in the skillful and effective culture of fungi by the Attiine ants ever arose and were fixed. The deliberateness and the monumental stability of the social evolution of insects becomes easy to understand.

Contrast this situation with a hypothetical human case, with the idea, or innovation—the "mutation" in the cultural society—represented by the discovery of a new approach, a new tool or a new technique. Here there is considerable historical evidence. Consider, for instance, the introduction of the domestic fowl into human economy.

Nobody knows how long it took Asiatic man to realize the potential benefits of the red jungle fowl or to begin the long process of its domestication which ultimately produced the barnyard hen. But there are interesting examples of the speed with which the culture of the domestic fowl has been taken up by savage peoples to whom the bird had been unknown until introduced by white men. It cannot have been more than a very few years after the introduction of the domestic chicken along the eastern coast of South America by the early discoverers, judging by their contemporary chronicles, that the knowledge and use of the bird had been propagated among native tribes over the length and breadth of the continent. Here imitation, and almost instantaneous imitation at that, was all that was required for the propagation of this new idea—this cultural "mutation." Its spread was unhampered by any mutual isolation of communities, by any time factor of genetic transmission, or by any restricting quality of genetic recessiveness. The brain and the technique of man alone were the vehicles of transmission. His imitative aptitude in cultural matters gave to the whole event an explosively dynamic character.

The spread in North America of the idea and technique of using the horse as a mount provides a similar example. It was probably less than a generation after the first of the proud Spanish horses had been lost on the American plains before horsemanship had become a recognized art among many tribes of the plains Indians, before the old dog-drawn travois had been adapted to the horse, and, most important, before an economic revolution had set in among certain tribes, bringing to some nomads of the plains an unparalleled ascendancy over certain hitherto superior agricultural peoples. Examples of the dynamism of this cultural neo-evolution, with its streamlined mechanics of inheritance which are made possible by the nature of the human mind, might be greatly multiplied.

The extraordinarily dynamic character of the cultural evolution of man made possible by such transmission of its basic elements is illumined by the fact that within ten thousand years mankind has equaled and in many respects exceeded the whole experience of the highest social insects, which certainly required at least fifty million years for its full expression. This represents a factor of five thousand in favor of the cultural development of man.

In biological terms this factor may be much more impressive. For in biological evolution the generation, rather than the year, may be the significant unit of time. In human life the average number of generations to the century may reasonably be taken as three. A generation of ants must be considered as the cycle between one queen and the first of her daughters in her colony that are also queens. This probably varies greatly among different ants. It has been found experimentally to be three years for the ant

Aphaenogaster picea in the artificial nest, and five years would probably be a conservative estimate.

On this basis, approximately three hundred generations of men have come and gone since the beginning of recognizable human civilization. But since the time of Eocene ants, which were already well advanced socially, about ten million generations of formicid queens have lived and died. On such a reckoning, the factor of five thousand becomes one of thirty thousand. The ants have, then, had roughly thirty thousand times as many opportunities to effect genetic recombinations and to transmit genic modifications as has man. The gap between the rates of the biological and the cultural evolutionary course of man himself is, of course, also great, and hardly less impressive.

This immense evolutionary dynamism of culture can accelerate, to an almost unbelievable extent, all the ordinary courses of evolution of the integrated society—the trends to complexity and to integration, the exquisite adjustment to the environment, the overspecialization of structure and overadaptation to habitat, and the rest—so that whole cultures can progress from simplicity to complexity and on to inflexibility and extermination within the span of a few generations of biological man.

How does this mode of cultural "inheritance" facilitate the close meshing of the integrated cultural society with the biological associative one? The genetic barrier which may prevent an associative society from behaving like an integrated one in evolution has never existed in the case of the human cultural society, and the latter has actually traveled far along the road toward such integration. But the converse effect of this situation is also important. The "society" of culture, although it shows much evidence of integration, may nevertheless partake of many of the qualities basic to the structure of the associative form. As in the associative form, the cultural society is open to growth by the accretion of new complexes of ideas that come into it from outside after they have attained independent maturity. Such ideas can be easily molded to fit the new culture within the span of a man's lifetime—indeed within a much shorter period. As in the associative form, a cultural society *need* not—though it often has—become rigidly intolerant of the addition of new idea-complexes, of new thinking men as members of its structure, or of the incorporation and the gradual assimilation of entire foreign cultures. It *need* not—though it often has—become rigid and overspecialized in development.

This is one of many characteristics of the integrated society of human culture which are compatible or identical with those of an associative biological society. This situation may have great significance. It may mean that within the social organizations of civilized man—and of civilized man alone—integrative trends can be combined with associative biological organization. Such a situation can confer immense potentialities for varied evolution upon human civilizations. But it may also expose them to all the dangers which, on the one hand, are inherent in the integrative form of social development and, on the other, may result from the inconsistencies which cannot fail to arise within so diverse and so hybrid a structure.

Thus the total picture of human civilization is complex and inconsistent. Its structure includes a biological family component which is relatively ancient in evolution, primitively developed, and normally exhibiting a rather low order of integration. Biologically man is thoroughly adapted to this ancient element of his society, even to the extent of showing some slight physiological modification in consonance with it. Human civilization further displays a typical associative biological component, analogous to the gregarious flocks and herds of lower animals. In its primitive state as represented by early man, this association was probably quite loose in structure. It has remained rather lowly integrated to this day depending primarily upon the over-all competence of the individual for group survival. Man is also thoroughly adjusted biologically to this type of social structure.

Then there is a third and an exceedingly important component of human civilization—the society that is human culture, the ultimate sources of which lie within the minds of men. This component has peculiar and indeed unique properties. In most respects it looks and behaves like an integrative society. In modern times it has carried the trends to complexity and integration, typical of such societies everywhere, to utterly spectacular heights. Yet it has never lost the capacity of meshing, in more or less complete degree, with the lowly integrated family and associative social structures of biological man. These it reinforces in certain respects while conflicting violently with them in others. To this new component man is still very imperfectly adjusted. In every part of his physiological organization save in his conscious intellect, man is still basically adjusted biologically to a much lower order of social integration. Whenever the culture society progresses very far along the road toward higher integration, conflicts arise between the intellect and the rest of man's biological constitution. These may have serious results for a whole civilization and for man himself. History is replete with examples of this sort of conflict and its consequences.

Viewing the structure and potentialities of human civilization in this light, what wonder that it is by far the most unstable, the most flexible, and the most complexly and delicately adjusted of all the social organizations of the world? What wonder that it is filled with contradictions, and that it takes all the skill of which modern man is capable to maintain its various co-operative and conflicting characteristics within tolerable balance? What wonder that its possibilities are so tremendous? It is indeed unique.

CHAPTER 13

The Modern Scene

HUMAN CULTURE thus has a double aspect. On the one hand, it embodies qualities that stamp it as an integrated social form, amenable to the trends and liable to the ills that beset integrated societies. On the other, thanks to the transmission of the ideas forming its basic elements and to other peculiarities of its organization, this culture society fits readily into the associative features of human civilization, enormously enhancing and enriching them. Many of the effective ties promoting the integrated aspects of civilization—communication, barter, trade, intellectual and cultural activities—serve as equally powerful stimulants to the merging of human groups and to other aspects of the associative character of the human social way.

There are notable examples of this in the political sphere. The incorporation of one state into another and the joining of several in a league are conspicuous examples. Basically this is an associative process. But almost invariably it is followed by a compacting to make of the loose and ill-federated entity a single, closely coordinated political structure. The formation of such leagues and their subsequent integration characteristically occur among neighboring civilizations in the face of a common external threat. Perhaps the most interesting case of all is the one most familiar to us —the league of the thirteen American colonies against the menace from overseas and the subsequent developmental stages of their delicately balanced integration as represented in the Articles of

Confederation, the Constitution, the issues of the Civil War, and the integrating influences of two world wars. The Constitution as it operates in the modern scene is one of the most successful of all attempts to find the optimum point of balance between the two social ways.

The roots of this curious duality are deep, and its social consequences have in many respects been spectacularly successful. But as the centuries have passed, individual man has been placed in an equivocal and an increasingly difficult position. Neolithic man could be at once a specialist and a generalist. Without too much difficulty he could span both the integrated and the associative way, since each was rudimentary. But ancient civilized man and medieval man were in a very different case. Human civilization had advanced with unprecedented rapidity a great distance on both roads. The gulf to be spanned by individual man was too great and the inconsistencies were too glaring for comfort.

Civilization veered from one extreme to the other. On the one hand, groups lowly specialized in character and almost like the Aurignacians in their generalized organization were evolved. At the other extreme developing states became so highly integrated that their own death knell was sounded through the inflexibility of their organization and the fundamental conflict of their culture with the basic biological nature of man. Witness the civilization of the Ottomans or certain phases of the civilizations of Egypt or Persia. Again—though more rarely—a single civilization oscillated between these two extremes, as did Rome at certain periods of her history.

As they passed from savagery through barbarism to civilization, individual men came to know an unprecedented order of physical security. But if they experienced this luxury, they were now exposed to a hazard of another kind. Never, in all their amazing growth from savagery to ancient civilization, were they to solve satisfactorily this problem of the curious dichotomy that ran to the center of their society. Never could they feel that one road might be followed to the exclusion of the other. For it was by these two distinct roads of integration and association that their very civilization took its being.

How much worse is the plight of modern man! He lives in a world where both the associative and integrative aspects of human civilization have reached heights inconceivable to the most sophisticated Egyptian or Roman. For human civilization partakes of that striking quality of integrative societies—its evolution tends to be auto-accelerative. So rapid has this acceleration become in our own society since the early days of this century, and so dynamic has been the expansion resulting from it, that individual man has had little time or occasion to ponder about the duality through which he lives.

Today, more vividly and critically than ever, we are faced with the huge problem posed by this aspect of human civilization, an aspect from which man has so long reaped incomparable advantages. Today the problem is how, without losing one's balance and sanity, to live in a civilization at once highly associative and highly integrative, to follow two different paths, often divergent, sometimes converging, sometimes crossing—two roads which we have traveled far and to which we are irrevocably and equally committed. There is no turning back. The gains have been too great, the evolution too long, and the relationship between biological man and his strange culture society too firmly fixed. There is no single solution. But there are gains to be made through understanding. No greater challenge has ever been posed to mankind.

The outstanding characteristic of human culture from Neolithic and possibly even from Paleolithic times has been the subtle continuity of its development. This fundamental continuity has long been obscured by separated events. Great civilizations which have emphasized one or another of the great features of cultural evolution have come and gone. Human culture has evolved at very different rates among different peoples and in different parts of the globe. These things have given to history an aspect of discontinuity. They have tended to transform it into a series of scenes in a great play which have been so contrasting that they have obscured its more subtle sequence.

Modern archeology and historical research, in disclosing the details of the daily tasks and problems of early man, have given us a clearer picture of how little human nature has changed through the ages, and how basically similar in kind, though very different in degree, are some of the problems that beset Cro-Magnon man in his villages and those that vex modern man in his cities today. In the last century, even in the last decade, human culture has advanced to heights never before remotely achieved in the history of human civilization. But the basic structure of man as a biological organism and that of the human culture "society" have not changed.

Can we say this with confidence? Has the real character of human civilization, then, not changed, but only become greatly intensified and more sharply delineated? Is there still a duality between the integrated "society" of human culture and an associative society to which biological man is more completely adjusted? Does modern civilization still show evidences of high integration coupled with those of loose association—those two modes of social living which elsewhere in nature are opposed?

The answers to this query in terms of modern society yield a plethora of evidence which renders a truly representative selection difficult. The indications that today's civilization is an integrated society of a very high order are abundant. But there is also striking evidence in contemporary life of the associative manner in which man still achieves his communal existence. The contradictions and the co-ordinations always characteristic of man's social living have both been carried to new and bewildering heights.

One of the most fundamental traits of integrated societies throughout nature is the oft-stressed trend to complexity in evolution. Consider the process of modern thinking from this standpoint. Thinking, ideation, and the combination and integration of ideas were apparently relatively simple in Paleolithic societies if one is to judge by the relative simplicity of the artifacts of that period which are available to us. By early Neolithic times ideas and techniques had accumulated in the culture, and processes of thought had apparently advanced immensely in complexity, consistent with the advancing richness of the idea-fields available to man, and with his richer technological environment. This increase in complexity of ideation and in the variety of combinations of ideas advanced steadily through the Bronze Age and the early Iron Age. With it went an increase in powers of abstraction. Human culture was becoming more flexible in the sense that its growing intricacy of organization offered a wider field for changes, as though, by remote analogy, it were a biological organism subject to mutation in the conventional sense.

It may have been at about this stage in human development, however, that a most important change occurred. This was the recognition of ideas as such—an achievement in abstraction comparable to the invention of the pronoun "I." With this concept went the further recognition of the extraordinary importance of ideas in human social evolution. When this momentous discovery was made, an organized search for ideas must have followed shortly —an intensive mining operation to discover and conserve the golden nuggets that man now knew meant progress. Historical evidence indicates fairly early attempts to segregate socially those men who were particularly distinguished by their ability to generate new ideas and to provide material sustenance for them so that they —like the metal workers of the early Bronze Age—might devote the greater part of their working lives to making this specialized contribution to society for which they were particularly fitted.

With this occurrence, the culture society had undergone a most significant change in its evolutionary processes. Hitherto, it had evolved like a wild animal. Among the random idea "mutations" which occurred within it, the best and most useful had been adapted and selected. But while unique combinations of these ideas had been achieved, ideas had not before been sought as entities in themselves. Conditions in which they might occur more dynamically and be selected more effectively had never before been deliberately set up. With this innovation, the culture society came to evolve more like a strain of useful domestic animals the breeders of which have paid close scrutiny to blood lines and constantly sought to improve the stock, which in consequence has undergone a dynamic modern evolution and diverged far indeed from its wild ancestors. This "domestication" of culture in terms of the organized search for ideas represents perhaps the closest approach of the civilization of man to the condition of domestication that has occurred in his history. Furthermore, with this development the *men* who had ideas useful in the social context tended more and more to be favored over those who had ideas useful primarily only to themselves. Thus communal came to supplant individual selection, with the consequent evolutionary trend to specialization of the individual which this implies.

But the development has gone even further. Today not only the selection but even the *causes* of the "idea-mutations" are under investigation. Few biological breeding experiments—save occasional modern ones dealing with artificially induced mutations— are comparable to this. The climax of the development, perhaps, is the process of modern technological research. Here the techniques of the origination, evaluation, selection, and recombination of ideas have reached tremendous heights. Since this methodology was developed, the evolutionary advance of culture has become as strikingly dynamic, relative to its older and steadier pace, as the evolution of the Brahmin breed of hen compared to that of the jungle fowl from which it took its origin.

This dynamic method of increasing the pace and the effectiveness of the generation of ideas is not confined to modern technology. It is quite as true in law and politics, literature and art, and the other myriad facets of modern culture. Universities, research institutes in arts and sciences, politics and economics, the research departments of commercial and industrial organizations, all specialize in this process. Closely linked with this development, accelerating it and linking it to civilization as a whole, are the ever-expanding means of disseminating new ideas by the network of periodicals and books, of radio and television, making possible the most intricate comparisons within the endless streams of contemporary human thought. This is a march to complexity indeed!

These, of course, are only the strictly material aspects of this neo-evolution on the frontiers of which mankind stands poised today. The brain of man, the nature of his culture, and the role of that culture in his civilization give him, for the first time, the immense power, unique in the history of the organic world so far as we know, of *choosing the direction of his own social evolution*—and of guiding it toward those goals. No living creature, so far as we know, has ever had that immense opportunity before—nor been confronted with so great a responsibility.

So far, modern man has exercised his new environmental control primarily in the field of material achievement. The tangible results in human civilization, of course, present ample evidence of a steadily accelerating trend to complexity. The evolution of human thought has been closely paralleled by that of human technology, from Paleolithic and Neolithic stone tools to jet-propelled aircraft, submarines almost independent of the need to come to the surface, means of radio communication so compact that they can be encompassed within the space of a wrist watch, antibiotic substances of unparalleled effectiveness against disease, an electron microscope that can disclose individual molecules and the smallest of viruses, a telescope that reveals the details of distant nebulae, and bombs actuated by nuclear fission or fusion so deadly as to make uncertain the future of a world at war.

Most remarkable of all, perhaps, is the application of technical methods of analysis and synthesis to technology itself. This is the analogue of the deliberate search for ideas as ideas. It has produced such things as tools to make tools, mechanical brains able to solve equations which could never be resolved by the human brain alone in the course of a human life span and with "memories" of marvelous speed, intricacy, and accuracy, and mechanical predictors to foretell accurately the movements of weapons after they are released or of storm areas after they have been formed. It has led to the development of the operational research methods made famous by the second World War—of research, in short, on how to do research. All these things, far more intricate than any technological conceptions which man has had before, have come within the last ten years. What wonder that the selective pressure upon the individual in the technological society of today has in many areas shifted from the older and more experienced to the young and flexible? For experience may be of little use in fields so youthful and dynamic, where plasticity of mind is all-important. If ten years have brought such a dynamic and directed evolution in the strictly material things what may the next twenty—or the next century—not show if our effort is turned, at least in part, to more wide-ranging fields, to the mind and the spirit of man?

Like life itself, civilization is continually further complicating the environment against which future civilization must develop. The development of more efficient radio communication opens up endless possibilities in art, music, geophysical research, and politics, and raises new legal questions. An electron microscope cannot elucidate any aspect of the structure and behavior of a virus, or even demonstrate its existence, without deeply affecting the fields of bacteriology and medical practice. Television has brought in its train organizational innovations in government and has markedly affected the whole field of the transmission and integration of information. In the immense complexity of modern life examples might be enormously multiplied.

As these processes of internal complication go forward with unprecedented dynamism, so also do the processes of diversification, equally characteristic of the trend to complexity, proceed apace, affecting technological, legal, and artistic spheres alike. Types of lathes in use in England and America differ very considerably, albeit the uses to which they are put may be essentially identical and the men who use them may have similar training and talents. Japan independently perfected forms of radar very different from those in use in the West. The various systems of modern television are quite divergent, though the final results achieved are very similar. Diversification has played so prominent a part in the evolution of our law that in many particulars the legal systems of the American states differ significantly among themselves. In the field of language every linguist will attest to the marked variants of the English tongue which are manifest within the confines of our own country, to say nothing of the divergencies evident in the British Commonwealth.

A fascinating facet of the trend to complexity in this connection is the extraordinary multiplication of professional activities in modern life. In response to the drive to diversification and to the ever-complicating environment of modern society, new social niches are constantly opened and urgent needs for novel professions created. It is not long since the occupations of psychotherapy and industrial psychology and radiology, of personnel management and public relations adviser and investment counsel, of design engineering and industrial quality control and new products engineer appeared on the American scene. Hand in hand with this development has gone the fission of older professions and branches of knowledge as the subject matter of these new divisions comes to occupy the full attention of trained specialists.

Closely linked with the modern trend to complexity is that other development so typical of the integrated society—the drive to integration. Indeed, the two are so intimately connected that often they appear as different aspects of the same phenomenon. Technical occupations which yesterday were the incidental duties of an all-around industrial man, to be discharged as a part of his daily routine, are now so intricate as to occupy the full attention of trained specialists. Old-time professions quite easily comprehended by the intellectual giants of another day are now so complex that the mastery of their minute branches requires the undivided efforts of many men. Thus in the nature of things it has become impossible for modern man to escape a specialization far greater than he has heretofore experienced. At times this specialization may become so acute as actually to be functionally reminiscent of the castes of the social insects. It follows, too, that a very high order of interdependence must be developed among such men. Men, so self-sufficient in Neolithic times, have for the most part become as socially interdependent in many aspects of their existence as the members of a termite colony.

These aspects of specialization and interdependence have sometimes progressed to an almost frightening degree. No better example of the extent to which they have been carried can be cited than today's technical industrial organization. Like any highly integrated society, such an organization must be well knit and able to compete successfully as a unit with other similar organizations. It follows that its over-all structure must dominate and be more permanent than its individual parts, and selection and conditioning of its members proceed upon that basis. It follows too, that there must be the highest degree of co-ordination among those parts, and that they must, in turn, be specialized in many categories.

First of all, there must be unskilled labor. From their ranks skilled mechanics and other specialized workers may be recruited. Then there must be a host of other specialized mechanical and technical workers—carpenters, metalworkers, founders, electricians, engineers of many types, metallurgists, physicists and chemists of several sorts. There must be photographers and specialists in photographic chemistry. There must be doctors—general practitioners, dietitians, industrial hygienists. There must be industrial psychologists to assure that working conditions shall be as good as possible in relation to mental health. There must be lawyers—general corporation lawyers, tax lawyers, patent lawyers—to safeguard those aspects of corporate life, to protect the corporation in competition with its well-integrated rivals and to permit it to advance aggressively.

Again, there must be corporate management of various degrees, ranging from foreman to department head to executive officer to board chairman—all representing specialized professions and trained by a lifetime of corporate work for such service. If the corporation is large, there must be a liaison class, whose job it is to co-ordinate the various divergent parts of the structure. Finally, there must be individuals representative of group interests within the organization, or between it and the outer world. Beside this integration of the modern industrial corporation, with the inter-dependence of its specialized members, the ant or termite colony is feebly and lowly organized indeed.

Human organization for mass production offers an absorbing example of this integrative development in a way of life which was originally in large measure associative in character. Fore-shadowed in this country in the early days of the Industrial Revolu-tion by Eli Whitney's conception of the interchangeability of the component parts of a rifle, this development has been deeply mov-ing in its breadth and intensity and is frightening in its ultimate implications. Through it the way was opened for the production, not of an article as an entity, but of its *standardized* parts—a truly revolutionary change in many social as well as technical aspects.

The consequences of mass production have spread far beyond the realm of industrial practice as it is ordinarily understood. They have invaded almost every field of human productive activity, in-cluding that last stronghold of the individual way—farming. Like the typical integrated society, the internal specialization involved in mass production and the efficiency which it has thereby achieved have given it great competitive advantages and have resulted in further specialization of parts and further integration of the whole at ever-accelerating rates. Indeed, there has been achieved what is in effect a social revolution in every country of the world where mass-production methods have been adopted.

Consider now the social position of the individual in mass production. In the truest sense he is a specialized cog in a machine, performing in endless repetition one job, or very few jobs. His work is not specialized on the basis of turning out one type of completed unit, as it was from the days of Grecian industry to comparatively recent times. This was specialization in its older and much cruder context. There the craftsman at least still saw his finished handiwork as a unitary accomplishment, and could understand how it fitted into the needs of his society, however limited its niche.

Now the task of the mass-production worker is organized, not around a completed *product,* but around a skilled or semiskilled *operation.* No longer can he take pride in his social usefulness as clearly epitomized in the product that his skill has turned out. The productive unit is now not one man but the sum total of the whole operating organization. Concomitantly, the social value of the workman, in his own eyes and in those of others, can no longer reside independently in his creative skill. Instead, it must now depend in important part on the position which he occupies in the organization, quite apart from his own capabilities or accomplishments. For without the organization he is useless. Quite as truly as the honeybee in its colony, he is dependent upon the organization for all his effective existence. He has become a highly specialized part of the typical highly integrated society, dependent upon the whole.

Anything more violently foreign to the associative nature of biological man would be hard to imagine. Yet this concept, spurred on in its evolution by the collective efficiency to which it gives rise, has invaded almost every aspect of modern living. Nowhere can a more poignant example be found of the potential dangers as well as the material gains of the integrative way in human civilization. Nowhere can one be found that illustrates more vividly the delicacy of balance between associative and integrative forces in human living.

The same picture of intense integration obtains in a survey of the wider panorama of modern society. As a structure modern civilization is more permanent than any of its components, far outlasting the life spans of individuals and dwarfing them in the sweep of its embracing tide. No more vivid example of cultural specialization and interdependence exists than the minute sub-division and the extraordinary specialization of modern profes-sional living. Strong forces of adaptation and competitive survival press the individual on to this ever greater specialization and to-ward the interdependence to which it leads, and force the society as a whole into ever-tightening integration. Such close integration has definite survival value in the evolution of the civilizations of man, as it has with all integrated societies—but only to a point, and that a critical one.

Like other integrated societies, modern civilization is capable of waging aggressive concerted warfare, as we know all too well. Indeed, the state of a nation in modern war probably represents one of the most extreme forms of integration to which the human race has ever been committed. Again, like other integrated so-cieties, the structure of modern civilization has definite bonds to maintain the cohesion of its parts, and these are developed to a degree suggestive of the state of the siphonophoran colony. No other integrated society possesses systems of communication de-veloped to anything like the degree of those of men. No other animal society, no matter how high its integration, possesses a specialized caste concerned with the transmission of information, much less any such caste as the developing profession in modern society of the co-ordinator of such information—the columnist with respect to current news, and the reviewer and abstracter with respect to information of a technical character. No other integrated society can approach the human one in the complexity of the in-formation which can be transmitted over its communication sys-tems, or in the speed with which such information can be conveyed.

It is amply evident that modern human civilization possesses to a marked degree the characteristics typical of an integrated society. Not only this, but the heights of integration which it has attained are in many respects greater and more irrevocably special-ized than those achieved by any other society in the world, in-cluding those social organizations which are often regarded as representing the peak of specialized integration—the higher social insects. Such has been the power of the culture "society" in influencing and overlaying the associative characteristics of biological man.

Nevertheless, human civilization still combines associative and family social forms with the integrated mode. Indeed, the associative, like the integrated, aspects of man's social life, have become enormously heightened in modern civilization, however inconsistent such a development may seem, and sometimes actually is. Most remarkable of all, many of the very devices of human culture which have so intensified the integrated characteristics of modern civilization—communication, trade, education, the dissemination of specialized skills, and the interchange of modern science and technology—have also carried the associative aspects of human living to heights undreamed of in earlier times.

Today we are deeply concerned about the apparent diminution of the importance and the integrity of family life in the contemporary American scene. Analysis of this problem, however, makes it clear that, while this mode of human living has suffered in competition with the integrated aspects of civilization in special circumstances, these commonly refer only to specialized and usually highly urban environments, in which the integrated mode of living is dominant. The obverse of the picture is more clear. The familial mode of human living has perhaps never been so secure and has perhaps never flourished so abundantly as in our civilization. It is nourished by all sorts of devices borrowed from the integrated society of human culture or resulting from its activities—customs of protection and sanctity, relative economic security, and material benefits of many kinds. If the protection and relative permanence of the human family in modern civilization is compared with its instability and its position of subordination in some other cultures, the conclusion is emphasized that the family portion of human civilization may grow in prominence and may become stabilized and reinforced by the heightening of the integrated culture society.

But it is in the associative portion of social living that this unique contemporary development and mutual support of normally incompatible methods of social existence in one civilization becomes most striking. The associative phase of man's social life is particularly adapted to a dynamically expanding economy, to times when man's control over nature is rapidly increasing—when his whole horizon is enlarging and the vistas seem limitless. Dependent as associative living is upon the many-faceted and generalized competences of the members of a society, it is well adapted to exploiting varied environments but is rather poorly adapted to exploring any one aspect of them exhaustively or to tapping a simple, unified environment to the utmost. The associative society is at its best in a rapidly changing situation, where it can make best use of its varied, flexible, but also relatively unspecialized potentialities. It is at its worst in a static and increasingly impoverished situation.

Perhaps this is why the associative method of living is so prominent in our modern western civilization. While material frontiers have largely ceased to expand, frontiers of the mind, of our economy, and of our control of nature have been advancing more rapidly than ever before.

Man's predominantly gregarious nature and the degree to which it finds expression in and colors the most modern and highly integrated aspects of contemporary social life are vividly illustrated by the way in which cities are formed and grow. Although in their internal structure cities vividly exhibit the effects of the integrative aspects of modern civilization, they are built up largely as associative structures. Though the population of every city increases in part through the children born within it, in the great cities this increase is unimportant compared with the increment resulting from the people who arrive there as adults from the country or from smaller towns and are drawn by forces that are essentially gregarious in nature. Not only cities but many other of our highly integrated social institutions are nevertheless built up associatively. Thus large businesses and highly organized professional societies, however well integrated they may be, are formed in the first instance by the spontaneous aggregation of mature individuals—a typical characteristic of the associative society.

If this unique modern union between the associative way of life and an integrated society is productive of inconsistencies and contradictions in the institutional sphere to an unparalleled degree, it has even more potentially dangerous effects on the unfortunate individual. He must attempt to travel along two paths that grow longer, more tangled, and at the same time more divergent. The problems which this contradictory situation poses are urgent. They affect us all in varying degree.

In any flourishing society the lot of the individual is made more secure and his potential opportunities are increased because of the accumulated margin of vitality of the social organization. This is as true among invertebrate societies as it is among those of men. Thus in colonies of termites and ants the margin of vitality of the community, in terms of protection and security from outside attack, of stored supplies of food, and of an efficient organization for the gathering of new food, is so great that such communities can support a wealth of unproductive and essentially useless pets and parasites. Such communities can subsist successfully on the basis of a very low average output of work on the part of the individual members. Ants, for example, are known to spend a surprisingly large proportion of their time in sleep or in idling about the nest and burnishing their armor.

This same margin of vitality has characterized human communities since ancient times. In older civilizations it was often exploited in the fashion typical of the social insects—in the support of inordinate numbers of essentially parasitic individuals and social groups, such as the Spanish religious orders already cited and various parasitic master or slaveowner groups which have been characteristic of many human societies.

Today, the margin of vitality accumulated by modern technological civilization is greater than it has ever been. At the same time, social parasitism is probably under better control than it was in many earlier civilizations. As a result, the opportunities offered to the individual for leisure and for broadened development have perhaps never been so extensive as at present. This is well illustrated by the reduction in the hours of work required to earn a living in the course of American history. Probably no pioneer of colonial America would have been willing to grant that anything less than toil from dawn to dark on every day except Sunday would have made possible the conquering of a wilderness and the establishment of an American civilization—and he would have been wholly right. No American industrial worker of 1850 would have thought of asking for an eight-hour day, for an eight-hour day at that stage of the development of the nation might have meant a serious setback in economic progress.

That fact, however little recognized explicitly, was subconsciously widely emphasized. Yet today a demand for a still shorter day arises constantly, and it may not be inconsistent with national prosperity in times of assured peace. This increased margin is equally well attested by the comparative number of hours of labor required to assure an adequate livelihood to an individual in a highly evolved technological civilization compared to the lot of a member of a contemporary primitive one.

But what of this leisure time and this enhanced margin of vitality? What of its effect on the individual? How shall it be used? Theoretically, it offers the individual unparalleled opportunities for personal expansion. For if leisure is combined with available educational facilities and with other opportunities for individual expansion—with percipient existence at the center of a web of many specialties—that margin may be turned to stupendously good account. The advance of individual man may become auto-accelerative indeed. But there are grave human hazards to the accomplishment of this process. Many of them are inherent in other facets of the very integrative aspects of modern technological civilization which make the attainment of the margin itself possible.

Notable among these dangers to the individual is the excessive degree, already emphasized, to which occupational specialization has sometimes been carried. Each of us, as he perfects his specialty, is encouraged to understand, and ultimately may come to feel, that his value to society lies in and only in his specialty. If he is proficient—so proficient that he can successfully compete with others in the same line—he has made his contribution. He has fairly earned his livelihood, and society requires nothing further from him. He may then use the margin of vitality to abrogate further responsibility, to sleep like the ant, or to engage in activities wholly unproductive either to himself or to his group, which consume time but offer little challenge to his more generalized faculties.

The more highly and narrowly specialized the individual is in his occupational life, the greater may become the temptation to take this line of least resistance. The drive to keep abreast of other aspects of the complex life about him may diminish. This attitude is fostered by various factors in individual experience. There is the prolonged and necessarily narrowing education required for entrance into the more specialized professions, which is apt to inculcate firmly in the student the habit of isolation from the world beyond his specialty. There is the further and further splitting of areas of skill, and the creation of a sort of incipient "caste" situation among individuals in terms of natural aptitudes.

This is perhaps the most viciously dangerous aspect of modern human civilization. For when the individual forgets that it is his solemn duty to himself and to his society to be both a specialist and a generalist, he has denied his basic biological nature as a lowly integrated social organism, he may have set up deep and dangerous conflicts within his own character, and he has left unfilled an important gap in social living.

Not only is this consequence of the integrative aspect of modern human civilization of the greatest potential danger to the individual. It is also hazardous to the society. When an individual resigns all concern in living beyond his narrow specialty and abrogates wider responsibilities, he undergoes the functional equivalent of the loss mutations which characterize the specialized individuals of those biologically integrated societies already discussed. In areas outside his specialty his competences may decline markedly. He may become ever less inclined to exercise them, and, indeed, he may actually become less capable of doing so. This derogation of the co-ordinative spheres of activity that are so indispensable to a democratic state may eventuate in their complete abrogation. They may then drift into the hands of those sufficiently powerful and aggressive to win such responsibilities. It is all too likely that such men will use them for purposes of self-interest.

When the individual worker has so limited himself, he has made a dangerously close approach to the status of the slave or the caste member in older societies. In the truest sense of the word, he has become a wage slave. This is not through any material oppression to which he has been brought by the industrial system. Rather it is through the psychological impoverishment which it has wrought. This same impoverishment can be achieved by other means—through grinding poverty and unremitting toil, as it clearly has been in many totalitarian states, ancient and modern. When the psychological impoverishment of the technological worker in a democracy has sunk to this level, he has in fact reached a dangerous kinship of viewpoint with the specialized worker of a totalitarian state. Then the transition of attitude involved in passing from one form of government to the other may not be so very great. He has taken on the typical status of the individual in a biologically highly integrated society. And, as has been earlier pointed out, the dividing line between the individual in such a society and the parasite on that society may be tenuous indeed.

Extreme specialization of activity and viewpoint is not the only means by which the member of a highly integrated modern society may undergo those psychological losses which bring his status perilously close to that of the social parasite. Total unemployment and the necessary social protection involved may achieve the same result. In the loss of morale, of the will to adjust and of mental tone which follows this experience on the part of many unfortunates there is poignant witness of the danger to the individual, not only of overspecialization, but of social uselessness, which may bring with it a feeling of futility and a fatal loss of self-respect.

We are faced with a very real danger that the integrative aspects of modern man's social life may get out of hand, as it were, and dominate his whole social and political structure. This is perhaps the greatest hazard of our times. It is a hazard because there can be no doubt that such a hypertrophied expression of the integrative tendencies of human society contains inherent contradictions and weaknesses which make it ruinous to the happiness of man and even to the continued stable existence of his societies.

CHAPTER 14

The Totalitarian State

PERHAPS NO greater challenge has ever been posed to the will and the courage of free men than that presented by the spread of the totalitarian philosophy in the contemporary world. Only yesterday free men fought in a total struggle to turn back the sweeping tide of the most powerful and aggressive exposition of that philosophy the world has ever known. Exhausted and bewildered, they were almost immediately confronted by another expression of the same philosophy, but one of a somewhat different character. This time the motivating element was not altogether an appeal to fear. This time it was and is partly an appeal to weariness. It is an appeal to the citizen to surrender the responsibilities of a competent individuality, to yield in the fight to be self-maintaining, and to delegate the struggle for survival to the integrated state. Like the parasite or the individual in the integrated biological society, the urge is to undergo losses in the psychological sphere, until—again like the member of the biological integrated society—the part is wholly dependent upon the whole, and the whole assumes the primary responsibilities incident to survival.

This is an especially sinister approach. It has much appeal to war-weary and poverty-stricken men, and the other aspect of the picture is not immediately evident. There are many half-formed philosophical arguments to support it. Leninists and Stalinists today will argue that man and his social evolution have no relation to the rest of nature, that man is a being specially created *de novo*.

This pre-Darwinian view—an ancient one of pure mysticism—is of course negated by every situation which has been examined in this book. It is far from peculiarly communist. Indeed, it is borrowed from ancient thought. But it contrasts strangely with the dialectical materialism which Leninists and Stalinists profess to inherit from Marx. Not long ago, however, when these philosophers really did profess a type of materialism, they argued vehemently that the way of ever-increasing social integration is the way of all developing societies, and that the further it is carried the more perfect is the state. To prove their point they might have quoted all the examples of evolving integrated societies examined in this book and many more. They might have told us that total social integration is inevitable in the human sphere, as it has been inevitable in the development of the Portuguese man-of-war and among the social insects. They might have told us, as they were in fact constantly reiterating, that this development is the coming one and that we had better climb aboard. In all this argument, however, they neglected to point out that in the development of an integrated society, selection and evolution of its members take place, not on the basis of their individual merit and advantage, but in a pattern to promote so far as possible the welfare and success of *a few individuals* within that society—the queens of ants and bees, the rulers of a totalitarian state. They omitted any mention of associative social forms or of the manner in which these evolve. They neglected the duality of human civilization.

The practice of totalitarianism undoubtedly embodies in the political sphere the acme of the development to integration which is so prominent a characteristic of many aspects of the society of culture. It seeks to attain the end-point of this integrative development and to make it universally comprehensive of the activities of man. It seeks the condition of civilization in which the organized political group that is a state has taken on essentially all the characteristics of the tightly knit integrated biological unit. The group is to have a new personality of its own, in which the personalities of its citizens are to be completely submerged. In consonance with this, the state and its authorities alone are to be self-sufficient in a generalized sense.

The relation of the individual to the group is to be governed by the theory that ideally every member of the totalitarian society, if he is to be allowed to survive, must be of positive use to the state and dependent on it. It is not enough that he be merely self-supporting and harmless, as in the democratic society. The value cannot be neutral—it must be positive. That is the typical dictum of the biological integrated society in evolution. How completely the integrative aspects of the human culture society have, consciously or unconsciously, been carried over in the totalitarian mind into the whole range of civilization is vividly attested by forty years of arrogance in the Kultur of Imperial and Nazi Germany. There can be no doubt that, in the mind of the sincere totalitarian philosopher, as opposed to that greater group who have a vested interest in totalitarianism, integration is the ideal. The more completely integrated the social state of man, the more closely it approaches a theoretical perfection.

Is total integration then an inevitable development among the societies of men?

First of all, it is clear that the highly integrated form of government is by no means a recent innovation in human affairs. Rather it represents a revival of—and actually a regression to—a very ancient governmental system. When the aggressive petty kings of the pre-Dynastic period in Egypt brought about the conquests and political unifications which finally resulted in the kingdoms of Upper and Lower Egypt, and when these principalities were in turn consolidated, this land, so uniform in character, and in its use so sharply defined geographically by the extent of seepage from the river that supported it, was united under a political system which in its very essence was immensely highly integrated. In theory, this vast domain belonged to the Pharaoh—the absolute governing head—to whom its produce was due in tribute. Surrounding him was a close-knit nobility. Appointed by him and holding office at his pleasure, these ministers of state and the governors of the provinces were in turn the owners of landed estates which were organized as miniatures of the royal household. Specialist craftsmen and industrial workers were attached to the household of the Pharaoh, supported entirely by him and furnished with tools from his store. In turn, they owed him what they produced. They were apparently bound to their occupations for a lifetime, and it seems likely that such professions early came to be inherited, so that an individual might be born into a fixed caste. Thus, as early as 3000 B.C. the integrated system of government was well established, and its efficiencies were being highly exploited in the peculiar situations to which it was best suited. Thirty-three hundred years later the last emperors of Rome, valiantly attempting to entrench their failing empire against the disaster inherent in the static and closed economy of the time, introduced a form of state centralization close to the ancient Oriental pattern, and even closer to that proclaimed as novel by the Nazi state.

This fact—that the totalitarian and highly integrated state is one of the oldest forms in the history of civilized man and has recurred again and again—permits some extremely interesting and significant observations on the kinds of situations which normally seem to evoke it and the environment to which it must be assumed to be well adapted. Total integration and centralization seem to have commonly arisen in human history under at least three general conditions which, while they may not be the only situations to which such systems are applicable, would seem to be among those to which it is particularly suited.

The first of these situations is the uniform, relatively simple, stable, and essentially closed environment, where previously there has been violent internecine strife which has wasted the substance of the closed economy. Under these conditions, strong centralization tends to reduce this waste on the one hand, and on the other contributes toward extracting the maximum return from a living situation at best meager and showing little promise of expansion to match the needs of an expanding population. In such situations,

totalitarian regimes may tend to favor intensive exploitation of
natural resources, where extensive exploitation does not appear
possible. The centralization of early Egypt under the Old Kingdom is an excellent example in point. Another may be the unifi-
cation of the Japanese nobles under the power of the Tokugawas.
This development is clearly antithetical to human freedom. Yet it
undoubtedly may do much, in strong and capable hands, to eliminate the wastage due to internecine strife, and favors the intensive
exploitation of the meager resources of a tight, restricted kingdom,
which is becoming heavily populated in relation to acreage and
resources. These material virtues may constitute a strong political
appeal in circumstances of this kind.

The second situation in which a totalitarian form of government is commonly to be found is that in which a state has girded
itself for total conflict against a formidable foe. It is entering upon
a grim period of strife in which survival itself will be a function of
the efficiency of integration of the state.

An excellent example is offered by Sparta. About 750 B.C.,
when the problem of population pressure on the limited resources
of the land became acute in the Greek peninsula, the various states
responded to that situation in strikingly different ways. Corinth
and Chalcis seized and settled upon agriculturally suitable areas
occupied by less advanced people in Thrace, Sicily, and southern
Italy. Athens responded to the emergency with an economic revolution that ultimately became the political one for which she is
famous.

Sparta, hedged about by Greek neighbors and unable to
colonize overseas, embarked upon the dangerous adventure of
seizing lands from neighbors of her own political stature and military caliber. The result was the long and bitter struggle typified by
the First and Second Messenian Wars, and a revival in Sparta of
ancient Greek institutions that were on the point of disappearance.
There ensued a regression into a military form of political integration possibly as highly developed and as specialized as any
that the world has ever known. Though it failed in the end, it did

enable Sparta to survive for about three hundred years in a military situation of almost incredible difficulty, and for one brief period to become the acknowledged leader of the Peloponnesus. Characteristically, however, the rigidity of the system prevented Sparta from exploiting her opportunity for leadership in any significant way.

A modern example of this phenomenon, which is all too familiar, is provided by the totalitarian organization of the National Socialist state in preparation for total war with neighbors of equivalent stature of civilization. In relative rather than absolute terms, this situation bears considerable resemblance to that of Sparta. Again a state, situated in a central position on the land mass which it occupied, was determined on conquest of its neighbors and ultimately of all civilization as the readiest road to prosperity and leadership, just as Sparta endeavored to dominate first the Peloponnesus and then the entire Grecian world.

The third condition under which totalitarian forms of political organization may tend to arise and to persist is that of a violently regressive economic situation. A once prosperous and rapidly expanding civilization may rather suddenly find itself in a closed world. There is a firm ceiling on any further expansionist activity in terms of new territory, and it is caught in a culture and an economic system which, in terms of its population needs, is static or regressive rather than progressive. Under such conditions, states have not infrequently resorted to totalitarian government in their later days in an overwhelming frantic effort to exploit what was left of the diminishing national resources in order to retain something approaching the old-time standard of living, at least for a governing group and a capital city.

Such was perhaps the situation in Rome under the emperors, from the time of Nero on. Guilds of merchants and craftsmen, originally free associations formed for professional purposes, were made organs of the state and became compulsory. Their function became that of maintaining the supply of artisans, who were artisans by state command. Workers in all crafts were bound to their posts and not allowed to assume others. Technicians in the service of the government were not only bound to their posts, but were allowed to marry only into the families of fellow workers, and often were branded to identify them irrevocably with their castes. Recent examples of this situation were offered in abundance by the Nazi state throughout much of its history. They are to be found today in Russia.

These situations in which once-free citizens tolerate or even voluntarily resort to a totalitarian government, with all that it means in the sacrifice of human freedom and the negation of the individual, suggest two things. First, in historical terms, this movement tends to be a regressive rather than a progressive one. Second, the totalitarian form is particularly adapted to succeed amid closed and rigidified conditions, in which the chances for the average citizen to better himself, either through the geographic scattering of population or through the internal raising of the living standard for the individual, appear at a minimum, and the only road to any sort of salvation seems to be through a closer cropping of the already well-mown field, which is assumed to be best done through integrated mass attack.

On a short-term basis, there would seem to be a considerable measure of truth in this assumption. Closely integrated biological societies appear to be especially adapted to wring the last drop of nourishment from a fairly restricted environment. Their competitive survival with respect to other societies of like structure is in large measure based on the effectiveness with which they do this.

A sedentary, terrestrially located ant colony must make the best of the rather limited environment to which it has access and must exploit and defend it adequately if it is to resist extermination at the hands of its neighbors. A termite colony, faced with the even more severe economic stringency involved in the consumption of wood as its principal diet, is in like case. In both instances, it would seem that the irrevocable specialization of the members of the more advanced social insects, and their close integration, are effective in survival. For the ant-hill community or the colony of termites inhabiting a log is normally able to attain a higher population density than any solitary insect in so unpromising a situation.

The totally integrated human state, then—like the colony of social insects—may properly be regarded as primarily adapted to exploit the immediately evident advantages of a static environment, rather than the potential advantages of a changing one, to which it is ill suited indeed by virtue of its rigid specialization. Conversely, it would be expected that the totalitarian organization would be poorly adapted to a rapidly expanding situation, in which the generalized competences of many individuals are important in terms of territorial, economic, or craft exploitation, and in which individual energy, variability, enterprise, and initiative in the discovery and use of new resources and opportunities are at a premium. Indeed, it appears that totalitarian forms actually rarely appear at this stage in the development of states. Common apprehension of this may lead the dictators of totalitarian states, who have a vested interest in the maintenance of the *status quo*, to protect the organizations which they head from the disruptive effects of distributed wealth or from other forms of increase in the opportunities of the individual, even when they are inherently possible by virtue of expanding national power or wealth. There are many ways in which this can be done. Notable among them is the device—commonly used by dictators in our time—of representing a constant military threat from abroad to the peoples of their states.

This may have a double effect. On the one hand, it emphasizes the need for constant preparation for war against overwhelming odds—a war which can be effectively prosecuted only by dint of intense nationalism, which means an intense integration of organization. On the other, it makes it possible to withhold from the consuming populace a preponderant share of the prosperity which their energy has gained by diverting it into military channels and other public uses of the integrated state. This artificial impoverishment is a good self-protective device for the totalitarian state to apply. For to allow the individual standard of living to rise too much, to allow its gains to diffuse into the populace, might have a fatal effect on the totalitarian organization.

In all of these fundamental factors of its constitution—in its rigid specialization, in its adaptation to the exploitation of a limited and static environment, and in its ineptitude in a dynamic situation in which the scope of the individual is broadening—the totalitarian state stands in sharpest opposition to the democratic form. A democracy is at its best where the totalitarian state fails. This contrast is particularly vividly illustrated by some of the ways in which totalitarian states have taken their origin and the circumstances under which they have persisted.

Under rare and special circumstances, the highly integrated political state may arise in large part as an extension and a hypertrophy of the family form of communal existence, the transition suggesting in some respects the evolution of the social insects. It is possible that some of the patriarchal states of the ancient Orient belonged in this category. More often, it may simply adapt the already familiar terminology and philosophy of the family to justify and interpret the high degree of integration after it has been actually accomplished. Certainly feudal Japan belonged in the latter group, and the power that such a concept may have, and the degree to which it may dominate the minds of a people, is well shown among present-day Japanese, to some of whom the emperor even today is almost certainly still the "father" and even the deity of a vastly expanded family.

Commonly, however, totalitarian states are formed by the fusing of existing and usually more loosely federated associations, which are subsequently welded into strongly centralized groups in the interests of economic and political efficiency. The Old Kingdom of Egypt presents an excellent example of this development, and the Achaean League represented an incipient development of the same sort in the Grecian world. Perhaps the most striking modern example among many is that of the Prussian domination of the federated German states culminating in the Nazi political structure.

The fact that totalitarian societies can arise as the result of the fusion of independent and lowly integrated elements illustrates strikingly in the political sphere the duality of human civilization. For in this manner the integrative aspects of culture mesh with and are imposed upon an associative society. In striking contrast, as has many times been emphasized, biological integrated societies do not arise in this fashion. The uniqueness of the human case becomes even more striking when the internal developments accompanying the integrative course in the political sphere are observed to suggest so closely those of other integrated societies, however dissimilar their modes of origin and development.

Characteristically, an imperious demand for skilled specialized labor is made by the modern totalitarian state upon its citizens. This demand may be filled much as it was in the Ottoman and the Greek states, when the laborers were frankly slaves. Individuals may be examined for special aptitudes, and systems may be erected in which each skill, as it is discovered, can be exploited to the highest degree possible in the service of the state. Sometimes rewards are used and there is an appeal to ambition. Again threats, punishment, or even death, but most often exile to the lowest ranks of labor may follow a failure to develop the skill appropriate to the needs of the state. Examples of the extraordinary aptitude of the totalitarian state in selecting and developing skills in its service on an intracommunal basis occur again and again throughout history—in the Ottoman and Greek states, in later Rome, and in the Nazi and Russian domains. The degree to which this refinement can be carried was strikingly illustrated by the way in which chemical workers were selected and used in certain laboratories of the German I.G. Farbenindustrie before the second World War. At the height of this extraordinary development, chemical workers were actually segregated and assigned to different stages in the development of dye processes in accordance with aptitudes determined by their employers, who in turn, to all intents and purposes, were acting essentially as agents for the state.

Closely connected with this detection and development of specialized skills on the part of the totalitarian state is the insistence upon the permanence of the occupation once it is established. This development has the same adaptive end as the selection and rigorous training in particular crafts—the creation of highly skilled castes whose competence shall be at a peak within a particular occupational field. A hereditary fixity of such occupational castes occurred at various times in the history of Egypt, of certain of the Greek states such as Sparta, and of later Rome. The tendency of the military profession to become a hereditary caste in Imperial Germany is a striking instance of this trend, while examples of fixation of occupational caste were not wanting in Nazi Germany.

This is the positive aspect of the individual's development in relation to the totalitarian state. The negative aspect is even more striking. It is surprisingly reminiscent of the development of the individual in biologically integrated societies throughout the world. The totalitarian state may take definite steps to reduce markedly the competence of the individual in every sphere other than his specialized area and to rob him as far as possible of the generalized abilities which he may earlier have possessed, so that his dependence upon the social structure becomes sharply increased. This can occur in a variety of ways. One of the most obvious is the interdicting of the generalized occupations of co-ordination, planning, and command to all save a small minority which constitutes the controlling political group of the state. Thus all posts of real responsibility, be they in the political sphere or in non-political areas such as engineering or art or science, may be held by members of the Party. The danger to the ordinary citizen of mingling in politics is patent, from the dictatorships of certain Latin American nations to the vast political structure of Russia.

Another powerful method of reducing the sphere of the individual is the narrowing of his mental horizon. This may be achieved through the use of a number of devices. Prominent is the withholding of education from the great majority in the body politic, or—more effectively—the development of a policy of uniform mass education of a propagandist type about the nature of the state and the relations of individuals to it. This latter development is of particular interest in connection with the functional analogy earlier considered between the role of genes in integrated biological societies and of ideas in integrated culture societies. The integrated biological society may depend rather heavily for its structural integrity on the biological kinship of its members. The totalitarian state may acquire a rather similar kind of reinforcement when through propagandist education it seeks to indoctrinate the mass of its members with similar idea-complexes, which tend to depress their competence, to increase their attachment to the political entity in similar ways, and so to solidify the structure of the state. This may ultimately lead, as it has done in Russia, to the forcible suppression of thinking itself, when such thoughts concern unconformable ideas.

Allied devices leading to increased dependence of the individual on the body politic are the intensive compulsion to work and, often enough, the grinding poverty in which that work must be carried out. Both conditions may tend so to weary and discourage the citizen that he seeks relief in the simple retreat from complexity that is the road to dependent parasitism, or rather to that exquisitely specialized form of it represented by the role of the individual in the highly integrated society.

One of the most outstanding tendencies of the totalitarian state which is relevant to this picture is the suppression of that middle class of workers which forms such a bulwark in more loosely associated political groups. Sometimes this class has already been greatly weakened before the totalitarian regime has set in, and this may be an important pre-condition for the coming of such a political form. If the middle class is not already actually moribund, it may soon be made so, by the destruction of the rights of private property and the drastic political action taken against it. This needs to be done, for it is precisely in a sturdy middle class that the type of individual most dangerous to any highly integrated society will be found. For independent property owners are noted for their championship of individualistic and sometimes un-co-operative ideas, which are likely to react badly upon the tightly integrated state. Fewer of such notions may be expected to emanate from an unpropertied class that habitually follows rather than leads and may be ground by toil to a state of apathy or again may be supported in idleness by bread and circuses and supplied with uniform ideas to reiterate—ideas which coincide with the existing political ideology.

It is interesting to consider some further functional similitudes between an integrated biological society and a totalitarian state. In the initial stages of their evolution, each grows rapidly and increases in internal complexity. In this phase, the integrated biological society may seem relatively primitive and flexible, and the totalitarian state may hardly be recognizable as such. New mutations in the one case and new aspects of culture in the other appear in rapid succession and are selected to build up a complex of features which tends to adapt each social form more and more perfectly to its existing environment. As these innovations accumulate and become fixed, each social group takes its definite evolutionary shape, as it were. It becomes committed both to a particular environment and in large measure to the ways in which that environment shall be exploited.

Thereafter, the chances that new innovations will be more useful than harmful to the group decrease rapidly. There is a greater likelihood that new ideas will clash with the pattern already laid down than that they will contribute something useful to the rigidified structure. Once the totalitarian state, like the biological society, has reached this condition of high complexity and exquisite adjustment to its environment and in terms of the relations of individuals within it, it has become a bit of high-precision machinery. A very few critical changes, occurring either within or without, may demolish the whole structure. Accordingly, the totalitarian state, like the integrated biological society, sets up strong protective barriers against such changes. It may disseminate conventional ideas as propaganda to compete with and drown out novel and unconventional notions, or it may ruthlessly suppress the novel ideas by purges, or it may develop an elaborate and over-riding party line. Such protection against dissent, indeed, may well be indispensable to its survival.

At this stage of its evolution, the totalitarian state has by the same token become extremely vulnerable to any changes in its outside environment. For, just as its internal adjustments are most delicate, so also it may tend to lock into its external environment with a machine-like precision. Like the integrated biological so-ciety, however efficient it may be in a static situation, it cannot easily reorient itself when the occasion requires. This is as grave a hazard to the totalitarian state as to the biological society, for environments rarely remain truly constant for any length of time. Extinction can come all too easily.

The totalitarian state may respond to this condition much as it may respond to changes within its organization—by movements to preserve a static situation outside as well as within. It may build strong defensive walls and surround itself with a *cordon sanitaire* to protect it against the shocking impacts of a swiftly changing world. Nationalism, hypertrophied patriotism, emphasis upon terms derived from the relationships of the family society to the body politic—fatherland and motherland—may all follow. The flow of ideas across the boundaries of such a state is likely to be-come difficult. Finally, such a state must inalterably oppose any large-scale moves of an associative character, such as world co-operation. The rapidly expanding environment which such asso-ciations will produce is typically that in which a totalitarian state is least fitted to survive.

The totalitarian state, wherever it has appeared, has character-istically exhibited this sort of vulnerability. It has typically suc-ceeded brilliantly for a comparatively brief period—until the environment to which it is so closely adapted has altered con-siderably. Then it has characteristically entered on a static period and a subsequent decline—sometimes to be later rejuvenated from within, sometimes to perish entirely.

This, however, is but the meanest reason for the vulnerability of the totalitarian state. A greater reason lies in the contradiction which it poses to the associative tendencies so deeply ingrained in men and in the negation of all the moral and spiritual values guarded by the belief in the inherent dignity and worth of the human individual. It emphasizes once again, and all too poignantly, that while the culture society is integrated in character, and civilized men everywhere live in part through it, as one component of their civilization, there are sharp limits to the extent to which integration and specialization of the individual can be tolerated, even in the cultural sphere. In modern civilization these limits are often approached, and occasionally exceeded—with subsequent disaster.

The integrated culture society exists after all only in a flexible partnership with the associative aspects of human society, and either component can be emphasized or obscured as the occasion demands. But when the philosophy of total integration has entered the political sphere and the totalitarian government has been developed in accordance with it, that sphere will brook no partnership with the associative nature of human biological society, nor will it endure competition with the individuality of man. It is in this utter disregard of all the fundamental characteristics of human nature that totalitarianism exhibits its greatest and its most barbarous inadequacies. In disregarding the principle basic to human society that it is the individual that is the important entity and that the progress of man through the ages has been the progress of individuals, the totalitarian philosophy is not only guilty of its most heinous omission, but commits its greatest practical error.

The end of the road for the totalitarian state is as evident as the end of the road of the overspecialized organism—and quite as inevitable. History has repeated the tale endlessly through the centuries. The totalitarian state secures a shorter or longer lease on life by virtue of its close adjustment to an existing environment.

As that environment changes, it is inevitably at a disadvantage. In consequence it may slowly weaken. But frequently it has been more seriously weakened by dissident elements within the state itself. The biological nature of man will not be changed easily by suppression, by propaganda, or even by several generations of grueling hardship. The individuality of man was not molded in one or two or a dozen generations. It is the product of an evolution as old as the human race, and it is not to be denied. Sooner or later it asserts itself in the totalitarian structure, and it asserts itself at exactly the points where that state is most vulnerable.

Men will not be prevented indefinitely from generating or expressing new ideas that are out of harmony with a specialized state philosophy. Strong men and restive men, long held as slaves, cannot be prevented indefinitely from attacking in mass the delicately adjusted mechanisms of state structure that have kept them so long in bondage. It is to just such attacks that the specialized totalitarian state is most susceptible. The state responds with purges of the rebels—with strong efforts to protect its vulnerable tissues. Often the structure exhibits astonishing tenacity, and it may long resist the depradations from within. The assassination of Hitler and the overthrow of his government were planned, and the most assiduous efforts were made almost throughout the last war to carry out both actions. Yet they consistently failed, often by almost miraculously narrow margins.

So internal dissension may long be suppressed. But throughout history the combination of revolts from within and the changing environment from without have ultimately proved too much for tightly integrated states. Weakened on all fronts, they have fallen before a combination of more flexible, less specialized peoples attacking from without, or they have radically changed their structure from within.

This is the answer to the inevitability of the totalitarian state. To the plea that it is the wave of the future the apt rejoinder is that such states have been current for five thousand years. In reality it is a wave from the past.

CHAPTER 15

The Touchstone of Democracy

IN TOTALITARIANISM a philosophy of government seems to have been designed as a tool, not of civilization as a whole, but of the integrated culture society alone. It does not serve as a means to ascertain and stabilize the proper balance between the associative and integrative parts of human civilization. Instead it takes the integrative development as its proper goal, and it will brook no competition from the vast associative forces with which it deals. This, basically, is why it is fundamentally unrealistic. This, basically, is why it cannot serve as a proper governmental tool of human civilization in its truest sense.

The greater vision must lie along another path, the course of which takes due account of the dichotomy of man. It is a winding path, running now along the ridges of the integrated way, now along the shores of associative living, and now poised delicately between the two. Its course must be sensitively adjusted to the changing needs of man and the shifting balance between the conflicting aspects of his nature and his life. It is hard to define this governmental form precisely, harder still to predict its course. But its philosophy is to follow and to serve the needs of man as he is— not to mold him to some Procrustean ideological bed. Though difficult to define, it has a name. We call it democracy. Its task is the most difficult and the least defined in detail. Yet in grand principle it is the clearest of all the governmental forms that mankind has ever known.

A visitor from Mars, to whom the phenomenon of old age was unknown and immortality the natural order of things, visited our earth in a space-ship a million years ago. His ship could not land, but it circled the earth rather distantly for close to ten thousand centuries. Then, breaking away from our planet, it succeeded in returning to Mars with its puzzled observer. He reported what he had seen. His view had not been very good, for he had not come very close to the earth, but he had been able to detect the existence of an animal whose activities had become steadily more prominent since his ship had first arrived.

He had noticed this animal when he first came. At that time it was comparatively rare and lived in small, obscure, and scattered groups on the land masses of the world. For nine thousand, nine hundred centuries he paid little further attention to it. Then to his surprise he began to notice large discolored patches on the surface of the planet. When he examined them more closely, they proved to be dense masses of these animals, which he called men. Like the red spot on Jupiter, the blotches in time varied in size and changed in shape. Eventually some blotches gradually diminished or sometimes even disappeared, to be replaced by other strange spots composed of somewhat similar animals and their work, elsewhere on the globe. As the years went by, the celestial observer saw more and more of these spots. They increased in extent, with the smaller spots tending to fuse into larger patches. But the curious phenomenon of discontinuity continued. Many of these patches persisted for a few centuries or tens of centuries and then vanished, to be replaced by other budding spots, which might have overlapped them, but were of quite another color and shape, and looked quite different.

After a good deal of thought, the Martian drew his conclusion. He decided that all these patches—which he termed *civilizations* —were essentially the same in character, though they exhibited obvious differences in detail. They were all composed of the animals which he termed men. But it was obvious that each patch originated spontaneously, having no connection with any other patch, except that two that were contiguous sometimes overlapped and fused. Indeed, during the last years of his experience, there was so much overlapping and fusing that they began to look like a reticulate network. The behavior of these spots was purely cyclic. Through the centuries that he observed, all of them did the same things—appearing, growing, changing, disappearing. There was no hint of any progress except, perhaps, that the patches tended to get bigger as time went on.

So the observer finally summed things up for the enlightenment of his fellow Martians. There is a kind of man, he said, that has lived in small and scattered groups on the surface of the earth ever since I first arrived and began my observations. He did not change a great deal during the whole time that I circled the planet, and he was still there when I left, looking much the same. But in the very last centuries of my visit, a whole host of new types appeared. Though suggestive of the older form, they were actually very different. Also they obviously differed very much among themselves, and there were no connections among them except occasionally when they overlapped. Their most conspicuous characteristic was that they seemed to come together in densely packed masses, forming large discolored patches on the earth which were clearly visible to me. For want of a better term I called these patches civilizations.

These civilizations all behaved in exactly the same way. They appeared suddenly, grew rapidly in size and changed in shape like a cloud, then stabilized in form and persisted for a little while. Then, as abruptly as they had appeared, they vanished. I thought that the patches increased in average size over the centuries, and overlapped more often, but there was no other hint of progress. The monotonous business was still going on when I left, and I must say I grew rather tired of it. This sort of man is an animal that appears suddenly, grows into large aggregations, and then disappears. Presently, somewhere else, another species is generated and goes through the same process. We would not do things after that fashion here. But then, who am I, who never set foot on earth in all these centuries, to pass final judgment on the whys and where-fores of the extraordinary doings there?

The Martian presented a conscientious report of his findings about man. It was a full report. It documented carefully the details of all the patches that he had seen, as far as he could detect them. What was more remarkable, it coincided exactly with some reports that certain of these men were making about themselves when he left. For many years after, they continued to make reports in a similar vein. They continue to make them today and to believe in them too much, as perhaps we all do.

This concept of the evolution of human civilization as a series of discontinuous events, cyclic in character, recurring with little interconnection and little progressive change, is held by few modern students in the extreme form of the Martian. Nonetheless it is a tempting and a compelling view, which most of us probably hold more tenaciously than we either realize or would be willing to admit. It can be a very confusing and deceptive view. In a closer observation of the structure of human history in its broader sweeps it becomes less convincing.

The opposite of this viewpoint has been emphasized in earlier pages. What has been stressed instead is the subtle *continuity* which has distinguished the evolution of man from his development as an early hominid to his modern state. Many civilizations, some so brilliant and so extensive that they seemed indeed to be events independent in themselves, have come and gone. Yet it is clear that most of them were subtly connected and that each absorbed and used some heritage from those which preceded it. Furthermore, these great civilizations were not purely cyclic in character through the centuries. Each represented a peak in the curve of man's evolution. Following the succeeding dip, the next rise was often higher than its predecessor. In modern times especially it has been rare that the succeeding depression has on the whole been as grave. So if a line were drawn from tip to tip of the successive peaks, it would almost certainly trend upward.

This may be thought an arbitrary view of history, but there are many facts which can be marshaled to support it. Its primary interest, however, is as a criterion of the kind of philosophy which prompts such a view. What do we mean when we speak of this sweep of human civilization which is not only continuous but is also steadily advancing in its average course? What is it that gives continuity to our picture of history, in contrast to that of the Martian? It is the stress on the human *individuals* who make up the Martian's discolored patches rather than on those patches themselves.

The patches may come and go, but the individual remains. It is the *individual* who steadily advances through the evolution of human societies over the periods of time that span the birth and death of many civilizations. The terms in which that advance is conceived, moreover, are individual terms—the growth of mental powers, of social capabilities, of spiritual qualities of individual men. The criteria we utilize to measure the advance of civilization refer primarily, not to man as a social animal, but to the dignity and the worthiness and the inviolability of the individual.

The great heights of integration of which the human culture society is capable and its domination of the panorama of present-day civilization have too often obscured this basic fact. In the terms developed in this book, they have also too often obscured the fact that man is basically an organism that lives primarily through the family and associative forms to which he has been long adapted. He has never made the transition to the type of integrated society which has characterized such groups as the social insects. The center of gravity—if one may so call it—of his whole being is still the individual.

Man is not a social animal in the sense that ants are social animals. He lives in societies, and he has developed the integrated facets of his culture society to an extraordinary degree. But his fundamental motive in doing this must be to promote the welfare and to achieve the further advance of the individual. In that pregnant eighteenth-century phrase, he must be engaged in the pursuit of individual human happiness. Whenever he has forgotten this, whenever he has confused the means with the end, whenever he has imagined that he is a creature adapted to an integrated society like that of the social insects, whenever he has shifted the emphasis of his philosophy to that level—then he has achieved totalitarian ruin.

The means of integration which man has employed have by and large been extraordinarily successful in achieving their proper ends. Pragmatically they have been justified in the gains which they have made possible for the individual. These gains have made acceptable the hazards to which the means inevitably give rise. The margin of vitality which the integrated culture society has made possible for the individual has so freed him from the fetters of daily living that bind primitive men, and has so increased the richness and stimulation of his environment, as to be largely responsible for the steady advance of the individual over the centuries. These integrative aspects of the culture society have also secured him from many external dangers. By permitting him to build defensive walls when these were needed, and to fight defensive wars where necessary, they have given him peace and security greater than he has ever known.

Over and over again, to be sure, he has confused the means with the end. He has used his powers of integration to fight aggressive wars, or he has lapsed into stagnation and slow decay within the cuirass of his security. Forgetting that flexibility is the criterion of life, he has carried extreme integration into his government in the interest of security and has bound himself in fetters which ultimately have proved insupportable. States that men thought existed for their benefit as individuals have often come in time to dominate them instead until men came finally to believe the monstrous myth and ultimately perished. But every time that such a cataclysm has occurred individual man has emerged once more to try again.

Have civilizations then shown a real and consistent advance, dependent upon and reflecting the advances of the individuals that compose them, through these centuries? The evidence seems affirmative. Though it is difficult to prove the fact definitively, there has probably been a real pushing forward of mental and spiritual frontiers.

It may be permissible to question whether the towering geniuses of our time are of greater stature than the best among Cro-Magnon men. But there is another aspect of the question which is more significant. Like other organisms, the individuals in a modern human society are widely variant in their characteristics—and, indeed, this variability is far more emphasized among men than among any other social creatures. Thus in the contemporary world individuals can be found who resemble characteristic types of humans predominant in ages more widely separated than the whole of recorded history. There may even be Neanderthal-like men among us today, as in Cro-Magnon times there were perhaps geniuses comparable to the greatest that our age has produced. The biological evolution of man is slow, and it will not be hurried by the exigencies of culture.

The significant point, however, is not so much that a wide range of kinds and conditions of individuals that have marked many stages of the progress of man are still approximately represented among us today, just as the great spectrum of organic evolution in the large is still represented among living forms on earth. The significant point lies in the statistical frequencies of occurrence of the various types in modern as compared with ancient civilization. More particularly it pertains to the relative extent to which the activities of those types have been appreciated and encouraged.

The phenomenon of genius is not new. Egypt had her Imhotep, almost certainly as great as Leonardo. Ancient India and China had their scholars and their men of religion of immortal stature, as ancient Greece had her Homer. Such men have been with us since the beginning of recorded time. No condition of civilization can either prevent their coming, or on the other hand, accelerate it. But what of their reception? And what, again, of those lesser but yet gifted men—prominent in their own generation—who will nevertheless be forgotten a few years or a century after they have died? The contributions which geniuses and men of talent can make to their own civilizations are potentially enormous and of preponderant importance. But their value is decisively conditioned by the receptiveness of the civilization to what such men have to give.

Here it is that civilization achieves its truest advance through the individual, and the individual through his civilization. Basically, the process is one of selection. It rests upon the percentage of men called great in any generation who will be able to express themselves fully and to give of their best to the culture which has nourished them. To the extent that they are encouraged, freed for their best labor, and persuaded to give it, to that extent will they advance as individuals and thereby further the advance of their civilization. Conversely, the degree to which they can express their highest capabilities will characterize the extent to which the civilization into which they are born has already advanced when they arrive. This is the delicate reciprocal balance between the best in the individual and the best in his society which has characterized man throughout the ages.

When this picture is viewed in the large, it must be said that there has been continuous advance in human civilization. We must say, in all honesty, that the great man of the present day in our own nation and our own time is born into an environment probably better suited to encourage and appreciate the higher ranges of the spirit, the art or the science of which he may be capable, than were most civilizations of any other ages of man, so far as we can judge them. This, perhaps, is the best of all justifications of the whole complex structure of modern democratic society.

What, then, of the tools of government which our civilization must evolve to regulate its activities and permit of their expansion? The basic task is clear enough. Such a government must sanctify and enlarge the sphere of the individual. It must give him the maximum of peace and security. It must permit of his maximum personal development, for upon this the whole advance of civilization rests. And upon the advance of civilization will depend the opportunities for future men to grow in the same way in times to come. Its purpose must be to make practical in every possible way the dignity of the individual which is at the base of every great religion—most of all of Christianity.

The means are more subtle and difficult. On the one hand, there must be opportunity for a full expression of the integrative aspects of the culture society. For these activities have in large measure been responsible for the spiritual wealth and happiness of individual men. But the integrated culture society must be held within its proper bounds. In the end, the individual cannot expand to his full extent without world fellowship with his kin and the sort of world ties that are fostered by international science and technology and by international arts and letters. On the other hand, it is abundantly clear that we do not at present dwell in a safe world where unrestricted international approaches are possible, and a sane defense requires the protection that only a degree of integrated nationalism can provide. We must have as a tool for our civilization, therefore, a government which permits an optimum course between the associative and integrated ways of social living, which provides the maximum of individual freedom for creative effort, which can weld a highly integrated body politic when the stern necessity of defense arises, and which can de-integrate once the danger is past. The keynote must be flexibility.

It is not easy to set intermediate goals—goals that must flow and change, that cannot be defined simply, that must meet divergent requirements, and that must maintain a balance of good against evil. Yet it is clear, in view of man's biological and cultural constitution and of the course set from the beginning of his social evolution, that by this balance of two different social ways alone can individual man achieve happiness and full effectiveness. It may well be the only mode by which he can survive. The establishment of this point of equilibrium, and the constant re-determination of its nature, must be the task of an eternally inquiring, eternally vigilant, eternally democratic body politic. This is the touchstone of democracy.

BIBLIOGRAPHY

ADRIAN, E. D.: "Physiology," *Scientific American*, Vol. 183, No. 3, pp. 71–76, 1950.

————: *The Physiological Background of Perception.* Oxford, Clarendon Press, 1947.

ALLEE, W. C.: *Animal Life and Social Growth.* Baltimore, Maryland, The Williams & Wilkins Co., 1932.

————: *The Social Life of Animals.* New York, W. W. Norton & Company, Inc., 1938.

ALLPORT, G.: *Personality.* New York, Henry Holt, 1939.

ALMOND, G. A.: *The American People and Foreign Policy.* New York, Harcourt, Brace & Company, Inc., 1950.

ANDREWS, R. C.: *Meet Your Ancestors.* New York, The Viking Press, 1945.

ALVERDES, F.: *Social Life in the Animal World.* New York, Harcourt, Brace & Company, Inc., 1927.

Annals of the Amer. Acad. of Political and Social Science, ed. K. Davis, "World Population in Transition," Vol. 237, 1945. "Social Implications of Modern Science," Vol. 249, 1947.

BAGEHOT, W.: *Physics and Politics.* New York, Alfred A. Knopf, 1948.

BAKER, J. R.: *Science and the Planned State.* New York, The Macmillan Company, 1945.

————: *The Scientific Life.* London, George Allen & Unwin, Ltd., 1944.

BARTLETT, SIR F., GINSBERG, M., LINDGREN, E. J., and THOULESS, R. H., (eds.): *The Study of Society.* London, Lund Humphries, Fourth Impression, 1949.

BATES, D.: *The Passing of the Aborigines; a Lifetime Spent among the Natives of Australia.* New York, G. P. Putnam's Sons, 1938.

BATES, M.: *The Nature of Natural History.* New York, Charles Scribner's Sons, 1950.

BEADLE, G. M.: "Biochemical Genetics," *Chem. Revs.,* 37: 15–96, 1945.

————: "Genes and the Chemistry of the Organism," *Amer. Scientist,* Vol. 34, pp. 31–53, 1946.

————: "Genes and Biological Enigmas," *Amer. Scientist,* Vol. 36, pp. 69–74, 1947.

BELL, C.: *Civilization.* London, Penguin Books, 1947.

BENEDICT, R.: *Patterns of Culture.* New York, Penguin Books, Inc., 1946.

BERGSON, H.: *Les Deux Sources de la Morale et de la Religion.* Paris, F. Alcan, Seventh Edition, 1932.

BERLIN, I.: "Political Ideas in the Twentieth Century," *Foreign Affairs,* Vol. 28, No. 3, pp. 351–385, 1950.

BINGHAM, H.: *Lost City of the Incas.* New York, Duell, Sloan and Pearce, Inc., 1948.

BONNER, J. T.: "Volvox: A Colony of Cells," *Scientific American,* Vol. 182, No. 5, pp. 52–55, 1950.

————: "The Social Amoebae," *Scientific American,* Vol. 180, No. 6, pp. 44–47, 1949.

BOUVIER, E. L.: *The Psychic Life of Insects.* Translated by L. O. Howard. New York, Century, 1922.

BRIDGMAN, P.: "Science, Materialism and the Human Spirit," *Bull. of the Atomic Scientists,* Vol. 5, Nos. 6–7, pp. 192, 193, 196, 1949.

BROGAN, D. W.: *The American Character.* New York, Alfred A. Knopf, 1944.

————: *The Free State.* New York, Alfred A. Knopf, 1945.

BUCHSBAUM, R.: *Animals without Backbones.* Chicago, The University of Chicago Press, 1939.

BURNET, F. M.: *Virus as Organism.* Cambridge, Harvard University Press, 1945.

BURNET, F. M. and FENNER, F.: "Genetics and Immunology," *Heredity,* 2: 289–324, 1948.

BURY, J. B.: *A History of Greece.* New York, The Modern Library, 1937.

BUSH, V.: *Endless Horizons.* Washington, D.C., Public Affairs Press, 1946.

CALVERTON, V. F. (ed.): *The Making of Man.* New York, The Modern Library, 1931.

CANTRIL, H.: "Psychology," *Scientific American,* Vol. 183, No. 3, pp. 79–84, 1950.

CARPENTER, G. D. H., and FORD, E. B.: *Mimicry.* London, Methuen & Co. Ltd., 1933.

CASTLE, W. E.: *Genetics & Eugenics.* Cambridge, Harvard University Press, 1931.

CATLIN, G.: *North American Indians.* Vol. I and II, London, Henry G. Bohn, 1866.

CHASE, S.: *The Proper Study of Mankind.* New York, Harper & Brothers, 1948.

CLARK, J. M.: *Alternative to Serfdom.* New York, Alfred A. Knopf, 1948.

————: *Guideposts in Time of Change.* New York, Harper & Brothers, 1949.

————: "Varieties of Economic Law and Their Limiting Factors," *Proc. Amer. Phil. Soc.,* 94: 121–126, 1950.

CLAUSEN, C. P.: *Entomophagous Insects.* New York, McGraw-Hill Book Company, 1940.

CLAUSEN, J., KECK, D. D., and HIESEY, W. M.: *Experimental Studies on the Nature of Species. I. The Effects of Varied Environments on Western North American Plants*, Carnegie Institution of Washington, Pub. No. 520, Washington, D.C., 1940.

———: "Heredity of Geographically and Ecologically Isolated Races," *Amer. Scientist*, Vol. 81, pp. 114–133, 1947.

Cold Spring Harbor Symposia on Quantitative Biology, Vol. 9, *Genes and Chromosome Structure and Organization*, 1941.

———, Vol. 11, *Heredity and Variation in Micro-organisms*, 1946.

CONANT, J. B.: *On Understanding Science*. New Haven, Yale University Press, 1947.

———: "Science and Politics in the Twentieth Century," *Foreign Affairs*, Vol. 28, No. 2, pp. 189–202, 1950.

CORNER, G. W.: *Ourselves Unborn*. New Haven, Yale University Press, 1944.

CREIGHTON, W. S.: "The Ants of North America," *Bull. of the Mus. of Comparative Zool.*, Harvard Univ., Vol. 104, Cambridge, The Cosmos Press, Inc., 1950.

DAHLBERG, G.: *Statistical Methods for Medical and Biological Students*. London, George Allen & Unwin, Ltd., 1940.

———: *Mathematical Methods for Population Genetics*. London and New York, Interscience Pubs., S. Karger, Basle, Switzerland, 1948.

DALY, R. A.: "Geology," *Scientific American*, Vol. 183, No. 3, pp. 36–39, 1950.

DANTZIG, T.: *Number, The Language of Science*. New York, The Macmillan Company, 1945.

DARLINGTON, C. D.: *Recent Advances in Cytology*. Philadelphia & Toronto, The Blakiston Company, 1937.

———: "The Genetic Component of Language," *Heredity*, 1: 269–286, 1947.

———: "Genetic Particles," *Endeavour*, 8: 51–61, 1949.

———: "Les Plasmagènes," Colloques Internationaux du Centre National de la Recherche Scientifique, *Unités Biologiques douées de Continuité Génétique*, 8, pp. 123–130, 1949.

———: "The Chemical Breakage of Chromosomes," *Heredity*, 1: 187–221, 1947.

DARLINGTON, C. D. and MATHER, K.: *The Elements of Genetics*. London, George Allen & Unwin, Ltd.; New York, The Macmillan Company, 1949.

———: *Genes, Plants and People*. London, George Allen & Unwin, Ltd., 1950.

DARWIN, C.: *The Origin of Species by Means of Natural Selection*. London, John Murray, 1885. Reprint of first edition with introduction by C. D. Darlington, Watts & Co., London, 1949.

————: *The Descent of Man.* London, John Murray, 1885.

DARWIN, F. (ed.): *The Life and Letters of Charles Darwin.* New York, D. Appleton & Co., 1898.

DEMEREC, M., et al.: *Cytology, Genetics and Evolution.* Philadelphia, University of Pennsylvania Press, 1941.

———— (ed.): *Advances in Genetics,* 1947 to date. New York, Academic Press, Vol. 1, 1947.

DOBZHANSKY, TH.: *Genetics and the Origin of Species.* New York, Columbia University Press, 1941.

————: "Genetics of Natural Populations IX," *Genetics,* 28: 162–186, 1943.

————: "On Species and Races of Living and Fossil Man," *Amer. J. Phys. Anthrop.,* n.s. Vol. 2, No. 3, pp. 251–265, 1944.

————: "A Directional Change in the Genetic Constitution of a Natural Population of Drosophila obscura," *Heredity,* 1: 53–64, 1947.

————:"Adaptive Changes Induced by Natural Selection in Wild Populations of Drosophila," *Evolution,* 1: 1–16, 1947.

————: "Evolution in the Tropics," *Amer. Scientist,* 38: 209–221, 1950.

————: "Genetics," *Scientific American,* Vol. 183, No. 3, pp. 55–58, 1950.

————: "Heredity, Environment and Evolution," *Science,* Vol. III, No. 2877, pp. 161–166, 1950.

————: "The Genetic Basis of Evolution," *Scientific American,* Vol. 182, No. 1, pp. 32–41, 1950.

DOWDESWELL, W. H., FISHER, R. A., and FORD, E. B.: "The Quantitative Study of Populations in the Lepidoptera," *Heredity,* 3: 53–67, 1949.

DRAKE, S. G.: *The Book of the Indians.* Boston, Benjamin B. Mussey, 1845.

DRUCKER, P. F.: *The New Society.* New York, Harper & Brothers, 1950.

DUBOS, R. J.: *The Bacterial Cell.* Cambridge, Harvard University Press; London, Oxford University Press, 1945.

DUNN, L. C. and DOBZHANSKY, TH.: *Heredity, Race and Society.* New York, Pelican Books, New American Library, 1946.

EDDINGTON, SIR A.: *The Nature of the Physical World.* New York, The Macmillan Company; London, Cambridge University Press, 1929.

————: *The Expanding Universe.* New York, The Macmillan Company, 1933.

ELIOT, T. S.: *The Idea of a Christian Society.* London, Faber & Faber, Ltd., Fifth Impression, 1946.

————: *Notes towards the Definition of Culture.* London, Faber & Faber, Ltd., 1948.

ELKIN, A. P.: "Social Organization of South Australian Tribes," *Oceania,* 4: 44–73, 1932.

————: "Anthropological Research in Australia and the Western Pacific," *Oceania*, 8, No. 3, 1938.

ELTON, C.: *The Ecology of Animals*. London, Methuen & Co., Ltd., 1933.

ELTRINGHAM, H.: *The Senses of Insects*. London, Methuen & Co., Ltd., 1933.

EMERSON, A. E.: "The Neotropical Genus Syntermes" (*Isoptera Termitidae*), Vol. 83, Article 7, pp. 427–472, *Bull. of the American Mus. of Natural History*, New York, 1945.

————: "The Biological Basis of Social Cooperation," *Illinois Acad. of Science Transactions*, Vol. 39, pp. 8–18, 1946.

ESSIG, E. O.: *Insects of Western North America*. New York, The Macmillan Company, 1945.

EVERETT, M. R.: *Medical Biochemistry*. New York, Paul B. Hoeber, Inc., 1946.

FANO, U., CASPARI, E., and DEMEREC, M.: "Genetics," *Medical Physics*, Vol. II, O. Glasser (ed.), Chicago, Year Book Publishers, Inc., 1950.

FASSETT, N. C.: *A Manual of Aquatic Plants*. New York, McGraw-Hill Book Company, 1940.

FIELD, G. C.: *Principles and Ideals in Politics*, L. T. Hobhouse Memorial Trust Lecture No. 18. London, Oxford University Press, 1948.

FIRTH, R.: *Primitive Polynesian Economy*. London, George Routledge & Sons, Ltd., 1939.

FISHER, H. A. L.: *A History of Europe*. Cambridge, Mass., The Riverside Press, 1935.

FISHER, R. A.: *The Genetical Theory of Natural Selection*. Oxford, Clarendon Press, 1940.

————: *Statistical Methods for Research Workers*. Edinburgh, Oliver & Boyd, 1947.

————: *The Design of Experiments*. Edinburgh, Oliver & Boyd, 1947.

FLEMING, W. L. S.: "Contemporary International Interest in the Antarctic," *International Affairs*, Vol. 23, No. 4, pp. 546–557, 1947.

FLORKIN, M.: *Biochemical Evolution*. New York, Academic Press, Inc., 1949. (*L'Evolution Biochimique*, ed. Desoer, Liège, 1944)

FORD, E. B.: "Butterflies," *The New Naturalist*, London, Collins, 1945.

————: *Mendelism and Evolution*. London, Methuen & Co., Ltd., Fifth Edition, 1949.

FOREL, A.: *The Social World of Ants*. Translated by C. K. Ogden. Vols. I and II, New York, Albert and Charles Boni, 1929.

FRANKFURTER, F.: *Law and Politics*. New York, Harcourt, Brace & Company, 1939.

FRANKS, SIR O.: *Central Planning and Control in War and Peace*, Published for the London School of Economics and Political Science, University of London; Cambridge, Mass., Harvard University Press, 1947.

FREUD, S.: *Totem and Taboo*. Translated by A. A. Brill. New York, The Modern Library.

FROMM, E.: *Escape from Freedom*. New York, Rinehart & Company, Inc., 1941.

————: *Man for Himself*. New York, Rinehart & Company, Inc., 1947.

GALANTIÈRE, L.: "America Today: a Freehand Sketch," *Foreign Affairs,* Vol. 28, No. 4, pp. 525–547, 1950.

GAMOW, G.: *Biography of the Earth*. New York, The Viking Press, 1943.

————: *The Birth and Death of the Sun*. New York, Penguin Books, Inc., 1945.

GATES, R. R.: *Human Genetics,* 2 vols. New York, The Macmillan Company, 1946.

GESELL, A.: *Studies in Child Development*. New York, Harper & Brothers, 1948.

————: "Human Infancy and the Ontogenesis of Behaviour," *Amer. Scientist,* Vol. 37, No. 4, pp. 529–553, 1949.

GIBBON, E.: *The Decline and Fall of the Roman Empire,* Vols. I and II. New York, The Modern Library.

GLOVER, T. R.: *The Challenge of the Greek*. New York, The Macmillan Company; London, Cambridge University Press, 1942.

GORDON CHILDE, V.: *What Happened in History*. London, Penguin Books, Inc., 1946.

————: *Social Worlds of Knowledge,* L. T. Hobhouse Memorial Trust Lecture No. 19. London, Oxford University Press, 1949.

GREEN, J. R.: *A Short History of the English People*. London, Macmillan & Company, 1888.

HALDANE, J. B. S.: *The Causes of Evolution*. New York and London, Harper & Brothers, 1941.

————: *New Paths in Genetics*. London, George Allen & Unwin, Ltd., 1941–42.

————: "Evolution, Past and Future," *The Atlantic,* pp. 45–51, March, 1947.

HAMBLY, W. D.: *Primitive Hunters of Australia*. Anthropology Leaflet 32, Field Museum of Natural History, Chicago, 1936.

HARRIS, H.: *The Group Approach to Leadership-Testing*. London, Routledge & Kegan Paul, Ltd., 1949.

HARVARD UNIVERSITY COMMISSION: "The Place of Psychology in an Ideal University," *The Report of the University Commission to Advise on the Future of Psychology at Harvard,* Cambridge, Mass., Harvard University Press, 1947.

HAYEK, F. A.: *The Road to Serfdom*. Chicago, University of Chicago Press, 1944.

HEBB, D. O.: *Organization of Behaviour*. New York, John Wiley & Sons, Inc.; London, Chapman & Hall, Ltd., 1949.

HERRING, P.: *The Politics of Democracy*. New York, W. W. Norton & Company, Inc., 1940.

HIGHET, G.: *The Classical Tradition*. New York, Oxford University Press, 1949.

HINGSTON, R. W. G.: *Instinct and Intelligence*. New York, The Macmillan Company, 1929.

HINSHELWOOD, C. N.: *The Chemical Kinetics of the Bacterial Cell*. Oxford, Clarendon Press, 1946–47.

"HISTORICUS": "Stalin on Revolution," *Foreign Affairs*, Vol. 27, No. 2, pp. 175–214, 1949.

HOGBEN, L.: *Principles of Animal Biology*. New York, W. W. Norton & Company, Inc., 1940.

——: *An Introduction to Mathematical Genetics*. New York, W. W. Norton & Company, Inc., 1946.

HOOTON, E. A.: *Twilight of Man*. New York, G. P. Putnam's Sons, 1939.

——: *Man's Poor Relations*. New York, Doubleday Doran & Company, 1942.

HOWELLS, W.: *Mankind So Far*. New York, Doubleday Doran & Company, 1945.

HUDSON, P. S. and RICHENS, R. H.: *The New Genetics in the Soviet Union*. Cambridge I.A.B., 1946.

HUSSEY, R. C.: *Historical Geology*. New York, McGraw-Hill Book Company, 1944.

HUTCHINSON, G. E.: "Survey of Contemporary Knowledge of Biogeochemistry," *Bull. of the Amer. Mus. of Natural History*, Vol. 96, New York, The Amer. Mus. of Natural History, 1950.

HUXLEY, J.: *Ants*. New York, Jonathan Cape and Robert Ballou, Second Printing, 1932.

——: *Evolution, the Modern Synthesis*. New York and London, Harper & Brothers, 1942.

——: *Man in the Modern World*. London, Chatto & Windus, 1947.

—— (ed.): *New Systematics*. London, Oxford University Press, 1940.

IMMS, A. D.: *Social Behaviour in Insects*. London, Methuen & Co., Ltd., Second Edition, 1938.

——: *Insect Natural History*. London, Collins, 1947.

——: *A General Textbook of Entomology*. New York, E. P. Dutton & Company, Inc., Seventh Edition, 1948.

ITARD, J. M. G.: *The Wild Boy of Aveyron*. Translated by George and Muriel Humphrey. New York and London, The Century Company, 1932.

JEPSON, G. L., SIMPSON, G. G., and MAYR, E. (eds.): *Genetics, Paleontology and Evolution*. Princeton, N.J., Princeton University Press, 1949.

JEPSON, G. L.: "Selection, Orthogenesis and the Fossil Record," *Proc. Am. Phil. Soc.*, 93: 479–500, 1950.

JOLLY, A. S. and ROSE, F. G. G.: "The Place of the Australian Aboriginal in the Evolution of Society," *Ann. of Eugenics,* Vol. 12, pp. 44–87, 1943.

KAMEN, M. D.: "Survey of Contemporary Knowledge of Biogeochemistry. I. Isotopic Phenomena in Biogeochemistry," *Bull. of the Amer. Mus. of Natural History,* Vol. 87, Article 2, pp. 101–138, New York, 1946.

KEITH, SIR A.: *Essays on Human Evolution.* London, Watts & Company, 1946; American Edition, 1947.

————: *A New Theory of Human Evolution.* London, Watts & Company, 1948.

KELLER, A. G.: *Starting Points in Social Science.* New York, Ginn & Company, 1925.

———— and DAVIE, M. R.: *Selected Essays of William Graham Sumner.* New Haven, Yale University Press, 1924.

KLINEBERG, O.: *Tensions Affecting International Understanding,* New York, Soc. Sci. Res. Council, Bull. 62, 1950.

KLUCKHOHN, C.: *Mirror for Man.* New York, McGraw-Hill Book Company, 1949.

———— and MURRAY, H. A. (eds.): *Personality in Nature, Society and Culture.* New York, Alfred A. Knopf, 1948.

KOFOID, C. A. (ed.): *Termites and Termite Control.* Berkeley, University of California Press; London, Cambridge University Press, 1934.

KROEBER, A. L.: "Anthropology," *Scientific American,* Vol. 183, No. 3, pp. 87–94, 1950.

KROGMAN, W. M.: "The Man-Apes of South Africa," *Scientific American,* Vol. 178, No. 5, pp. 16–19, 1948.

KUDO, R. R.: *Protozoology.* Springfield, Ill., Charles C. Thomas; Toronto, The Ryerson Press, Third Edition, 1946.

LACK, D.: *Darwin's Finches.* London, Cambridge University Press, 1947.

LANGER, S. K.: *Philosophy in a New Key.* New York, Mentor Books, New American Library Inc., 1949.

LASHLEY, K. S.: "Persistent Problems in the Evolution of Mind," *Quart. Rev. Biol.,* 24: 28–42, 1949.

LASSWELL, H. D.: *The Analysis of Political Behaviour.* New York, Oxford University Press, 1947.

————: *Power and Personality.* New York, W. W. Norton & Company, Inc., 1948.

LEDERBERG, J.: "Problems in Microbial Genetics," *Heredity,* 2: 145–198, 1948.

LE GROS, CLARK W. E.: "The Anatomical Basis of Sensory Experience," in *New Biology,* 1, pp. 72–85. London, Penguin Books, 1946.

LEIGHTON, A. H.: *Human Relations in a Changing World.* New York, E. P. Dutton & Company, Inc., 1949.

LEWIN, K.: *Resolving Social Conflicts.* New York, Harper & Brothers, 1945.

LINDSAY, A. D.: *The Essentials of Democracy.* London, Oxford University Press, Fourth Impression, 1948.

LINTON, R. (ed.): *The Science of Man in the World Crisis.* New York, Columbia University Press, 1945.

LOBECK, A. K.: *Geomorphology.* New York, McGraw-Hill Book Company, 1939.

LORIMER, F.: "Population Movements in Imperial Russia and the Soviet Union," in *Compass of the World.* Weigert, H. W. and Stefansson, V. (eds.). New York, The Macmillan Company, 1944, pp. 443–460.

LOVE, J. R. B.: *Stone Age Bushmen of Today.* London, Blackie & Son, Ltd., 1936.

LOWIE, R. H.: *Primitive Society.* New York, Boni and Liveright, 1925.

LUBBOCK, SIR J.: *Scientific Lectures.* London, Macmillan & Company, 1879.

———: *Ants, Bees and Wasps.* New York, D. Appleton & Company, 1882.

———: *On the Senses, Instincts and Intelligence of Animals.* New York, D. Appleton & Company, 1908.

MC COOK, H. C.: *The Honey Ants and the Occident Ants.* Philadelphia, J. B. Lippincott Company, 1882.

MAC IVER, R. M.: *The Web of Government.* New York, The Macmillan Company, 1947.

MAIER, N. F. and SCHNEIRLA, T. C.: *Principles of Animal Psychology.* New York, McGraw-Hill Book Company, 1935.

MALINOWSKI, B.: *The Dynamics of Culture Change.* New Haven, Yale University Press; London, Oxford University Press, 1946.

MANGHAM, S.: *Earth's Green Mantle.* New York, The Macmillan Company, 1939.

MANNHEIM, K.: *Man and Society.* New York, Harcourt, Brace & Company; London, Routledge and Kegan Paul, Ltd., 1949.

MARKEL, L. (ed.): *Public Opinion and Foreign Policy.* New York, Harper & Brothers, 1949.

MATHER, K.: *Biometrical Genetics.* New York, Dover Publications, Inc., 1949.

——— and HARRISON, B. J.: "The Manifold Effect of Selection," *Heredity,* 3: 1–52, 1949; 3: 131–162, 1949.

MAYR, E.: "Speciation and Selection," *Proc. Am. Phil. Soc.,* 93: 514–519, 1950.

———: *Systematics and the Origin of Species.* New York, Columbia University Press, 1947.

MEANS, P. A.: *Ancient Civilizations of the Andes.* New York, Charles Scribner's Sons, 1931.

MEYERHOF, O.: "Biochemistry," *Scientific American,* Vol. 183, No. 3, pp. 62–68, 1950.

MICHENER, C. D.: "A Character Analysis of a Solitary Bee," *Evolution,* 1: 172–185, 1947.

MILLER, N. E. and DOLLARD, J.: *Social Learning and Imitation.* New Haven, Yale University Press, Third Printing, 1947.

MONTAGU, A.: "Social Instincts," *Scientific American,* Vol. 182, No. 4, pp. 54–56, 1950.

MOORE, B., JR.: *Soviet Politics, The Dilemma of Power.* Cambridge, Harvard University Press, 1950.

MORGAN, L. H.: *Ancient Society.* New York, Henry Holt & Company, 1907.

MOY-THOMAS, J. A.: *Palaeozoic Fishes.* London, Methuen & Co., Ltd., 1939.

MULLER, H. J.: *The Gene,* Pilgrim Trust Lecture for 1945. *Proc. Roy. Soc.,* Series B, London, 134: 1–37, 1947.

———: "Progress and Prospects in Human Genetics," *Am. J. Human Genetics,* 1: 1–18, 1949.

———: "The Darwinian and Modern Concepts of Natural Selection," *Proc. Am. Phil. Soc.,* 93: 459–470, 1950.

———: "Our Load of Mutations," *Am. J. Human Genetics,* 2: 111–176, 1950.

MURPHY, R. C.: "Antarctic Zoogeography and Some of Its Problems," in *Problems of Polar Research,* Amer. Geographic Soc. Special Pub. No. 7, pp. 354–379. Worcester, Mass., Commonwealth Press, 1928.

NEEDHAM, J.: *Biochemistry and Morphogenesis.* London, Cambridge University Press, 1942.

NORMAN, J. R.: *A History of Fishes.* New York, A. A. Wyn, Inc., 1948.

——— and FRASER, F. C.: *Giant Fishes, Whales and Dolphins.* London, Putnam & Co., Ltd., New Edition, 1948.

NORTHROP, F. S. C.: *The Logic of the Sciences and the Humanities.* New York, The Macmillan Company, 1948.

NOTESTEIN, F. W.: "Fundamentals of Population Change in Europe and the Soviet Union," in *Compass of the World.* Weigert, H. W. and Stefansson, V. (eds.). New York, The Macmillan Company, 1944, pp. 429–442.

OGDEN, C. K. and RICHARDS, I. A.: *The Meaning of Meaning.* New York, Harcourt, Brace & Company; London, Routledge and Kegan Paul, Ltd., 1948.

OPARIN, A. I.: *The Origin of Life.* Translated by Sergius Morgulis. New York, The Macmillan Company, 1938.

OPPENHEIMER, J. R.: "Physics in the Contemporary World," Second

Arthur D. Little Memorial Lecture at Massachusetts Institute of Technology, 1947.

PARSONS, T.: *Essays in Sociological Theory*. Glencoe, Illinois, The Free Press, 1949.

PEARSE, A. S.: *Animal Ecology*. New York, McGraw-Hill Book Company, 1939.

———: *Introduction to Parasitology*. Springfield, Illinois, Charles C. Thomas, 1942.

PEATTIE, R.: *Geography in Human Destiny*. New York, George W. Stewart, Fourth Printing, 1945.

PERRY, R. B.: *Characteristically American*. New York, Alfred A. Knopf, 1949.

PETERS, R. A.: "The Cell," *Brit. Ass'n. for the Advancement of Science*, 6: 257–266, 1949.

PLATH, O. E.: *Bumblebees and Their Ways*. New York, The Macmillan Company, 1934.

PLEDGE, H. T.: *Science Since 1500*. New York, The Philosophical Library, 1947.

POLYANI, M.: "Scientific Convictions and the Free Society," *Bull. Atomic Scientists*, 6: 38–42, 1950.

———: "Freedom in Science," *Bull. Atomic Scientists*, 7: 195–198, 1950.

PRESCOTT, W. H.: *The Conquest of Mexico and the Conquest of Peru*. New York, Random House.

RADCLIFFE-BROWN, A. R.: "The Social Organization of Australian Tribes," *Oceania*, 1: 34–63; 206–246; 322–341, 1930.

RAYMOND, P. E.: *Prehistoric Life*. Cambridge, Harvard University Press; London, Oxford University Press, 1939.

DE REAMUR, R. A. F.: *The Natural History of Ants*. Translated and with annotations by W. M. Wheeler. New York, Alfred A. Knopf, 1926.

RIESMAN, D.: *The Lonely Crowd*. New Haven, Yale University Press, 1950.

ROBINSON, G. T.: "The Ideological Combat," *Foreign Affairs*, 27: 525–539, 1949.

ROBINSON, J. H.: *An Introduction to the History of Western Europe*. New York, Ginn & Company, 1925.

———: *The Mind in the Making*. London, Watts & Company, Fifth Impression, 1946.

ROGERS, C. G.: *Textbook of Comparative Physiology*. New York, McGraw-Hill Book Company, 1938.

RONNE, FINN: "Ronne Antarctic Research Expedition," *Bull. Amer. Geographic Soc. of N.Y.*, 38: 355–391, 1948.

Roscoe B. Jackson Memorial Laboratory, Bar Harbor, Maine, *Conference on Genetics and Social Behaviour*, 1946.

ROSTOVTZEFF, M.: *A History of the Ancient World*. Oxford, Clarendon Press, 1927.

RUDMOSE BROWN, R. N.: "Antarctic and Sub-Antarctic Plant Life and Some of Its Problems," in *Problems of Polar Research,* Amer. Geographic Soc. Spec. Pub. No. 7, pp. 342–352, Worcester, Mass., Commonwealth Press, 1928.

RUSSELL, B.: *The Scientific Outlook.* Glencoe, Illinois, The Free Press,
———: *Authority and the Individual.* London, George Allen & Unwin, Ltd., 1949.

RUSSELL, F. S. and YONGE, C. M.: *The Seas.* London, Frederick Warne & Co., Ltd., 1947.

SCHNEIRLA, T. C.: "Study on Army-Ants in Panama," *Jour. Comp. Psychol.,* 15: 267–300, 1933.

———: "Raiding and Other Outstanding Phenomena in the Behaviour of Army-Ants," *Proc. Nat. Acad. Sci.,* 20: 316–321, 1934.

———: "A Theory of Army-Ant Behaviour Based upon the Analysis of Activities in a Representative Species," *Jour. Comp. Psychol.,* 25: 51–90, 1938.

———: "Social Organization in Insects, as Related to Individual Function," *Psychol. Rev.,* 48 (6): 465–486, 1941.

———: The Reproductive Functions of the Army-Ant Queen as Pacemakers of the Group Behaviour Pattern," *Jour. N.Y. Ent. Soc.,* 52: 153–192, 1944.

———: "The Army-Ant Behaviour Pattern: Nomad-Statary Relations in the Swarmers and the Problem of Migration," *Biol. Bull.,* 88: 166–193, 1945.

———: "A Study of Army-Ant Life and Behaviour under Dry-Season Conditions with Special Reference to Reproductive Functions," *Amer. Mus. Novitates,* No. 1336, New York, The Amer. Mus. of Natural History, 1947.

———: "Army-Ant Life and Behaviour under Dry-Season Conditions with Special Reference to Reproductive Functions," *Zoologica,* Scientific Contributions of the New York Zoological Society, 32: 89–113, 1948.

SCHUCHERT, C., and DUNBAR, C. O.: *A Textbook of Geology, Part II— Historical Geology.* New York, John Wiley & Sons, Inc.; London, Chapman & Hall, Ltd., 1941.

SCHWARZ, H. F.: *Stingless Bees (Meliponidae) of the Western Hemisphere.* Bull. of the Amer. Mus. of Natural History, 90, New York, 1948.

SEARS, P. B.: *Charles Darwin.* New York and London, Charles Scribner's Sons, 1950.

SHANNON, C. E. and WEAVER, W.: *The Mathematical Theory of Communication.* Urbana, Illinois, University of Illinois Press, 1949.

SIMPSON, G. G. and ROE, A.: *Quantitative Zoology.* New York, McGraw-Hill Book Company, 1939.

————: *Tempo and Mode in Evolution.* New York, Columbia University Press, 1944.

————: *The Meaning of Evolution.* New Haven, Yale University Press; London, Oxford University Press, 1949.

SMITH, G. M.: *The Fresh-Water Algae of the United States.* New York, McGraw-Hill Book Company, 1933.

————: *Cryptogamic Botany*—Vol. I, *Algae and Fungi.* New York, McGraw-Hill Book Company, 1938.

SNYDER, T. E.: "The Fossil Termites of the United States and Their Living Relatives," *Proc. Ent. Soc. of Washington,* 52: 190–199, 1950.

SONNEBORN, T. M.: "Beyond the Gene," *Amer. Scientist,* 37: 33–59, 1948.

————: "Partner of the Genes," *Scientific American,* Vol. 183, No. 5, pp. 30–39, 1950.

———— and BEADLE, G. H.: Colloques Internationaux du Centre National de la Recherche Scientifiques, *Unités Biologiques douées de Continuité Génétique,* 8, pp. 25–35, 1949.

SPENCER JONES, H.: *Life on Other Worlds.* New York, Mentor Books, New American Library, 1949.

STEBBINS, G. L., JR.: "Reality and Efficacy of Selection in Plants," *Proc. Am. Phil. Soc.,* 93: 501–513, 1950.

STERN, C.: *Human Genetics.* San Francisco, W. H. Freeman & Co., 1949.

STIMSON, H. L.: "The Challenge to Americans," *Foreign Affairs,* 26: 5–14, 1947.

STRONG, L. C.: "Genetics and Cancer," *Scientific American,* Vol. 183, No. 1, pp. 44–47, 1950.

STURTEVANT, E. H.: *An Introduction to Linguistic Science.* New Haven, Yale University Press; London, Oxford University Press, 1947.

SUMNER, W. G. and KELLER, A. G.: *The Science of Society,* Vols. I to IV. New Haven, Yale University Press; London, Oxford University Press, 1927–1946.

SYLVESTER, H. M.: *Indian Wars of New England,* Vols. I to III. Boston, W. B. Clarke Company, 1910.

TAWNEY, R. H.: *The Acquisitive Society.* New York, Harcourt, Brace & Company, 1920.

————: *The Western Political Tradition,* Burge Memorial Trust Lecture. London, S.C.M. Press, 1949.

————: *Social History and Literature,* Seventh Annual Lecture of the National Book League. London, Cambridge University Press, 1950.

TAYLOR, G.: "Correlations and Culture," *The Advancement of Science,* pp. 103–138, Brit. Assn. for the Advancement of Science, 1938.

TOYNBEE, A. J.: *A Study of History,* Vols. I–VI. New York and London, Oxford University Press, 1934–1946.

————: *A Study of History* (abridgment by D. C. Somervell). New York, Oxford University Press, 1947.

————: *Civilization on Trial*. New York, Oxford University Press, 1948.

WADDINGTON, C. H.: *Organizers and Genes*. London, Cambridge University Press; New York, The Macmillan Company, 1940.

————: *An Introduction to Modern Genetics*. London, George Allen & Unwin, Ltd., Second Impression, 1950.

WALTON SMITH, F. G.: *Atlantic Reef Corals*. University of Miami Press, 1948.

WEAVER, W.: "Science and Complexity," *Amer. Scientist*, 36: 536–544, 1948.

WESTERMANN, W. L.: "Ancient Slavery," *Scientific American*, Vol. 180, No. 6, pp. 40–44, 1949.

WESTERMARK, E. A.: *The History of Human Marriage*, 3 vols. New York, The Atherton Book Company, Fifth Edition, 1922.

WHEELER, W. M.: *Ants, Their Structure, Development and Behaviour*. New York, Columbia University Press, 1913.

————: *Social Life among the Insects*. New York, Harcourt, Brace & Company, 1923.

————: *The Social Insects*. New York, Harcourt, Brace & Company, 1928.

————: *Colony Founding among Ants*. Cambridge, Harvard University Press, 1933.

————: *Essays in Philosophical Biology*. Cambridge, Harvard University Press, 1939.

WHITE, M. J. D.: *Animal Cytology and Evolution*. London, Cambridge University Press, 1945.

WIGGLESWORTH, V. B.: *The Principles of Insect Physiology* (Second Edition). London, Methuen & Co., Ltd., 1942.

WILDT, R.: "The Constitution of the Planets," *Proc. Am. Phil. Soc.*, 81: 135–152, 1939.

————: "On the Possible Existence of Formaldehyde in the Atmosphere of Venus," *Astrophys. J.*, 92: 247–255, 1940.

————: "Note on the Surface Temperature of Venus," *Astrophys. J.*, 91: 266–268, 1940.

WILLIAMS, R. T. (ed.): "Biochemical Aspects of Genetics," *Biochemical Soc. Symposia No. 4*. London, Cambridge University Press, 1950.

WITTFOGEL, K. A.: "Russia and Asia," *World Politics*, II: 445–462, 1950.

WOODS, H.: *Palaeontology*. London, Cambridge University Press, Seventh Edition, 1937.

WOODWARD, E. L.: "The Heritage of Western Civilization," *International Affairs*, 25: 137–148, 1949.

WRIGHT, S.: "The Physiology of the Gene," *Physiol. Rev.*, 21: 487–527, 1941.

————: "Population Trends and International Relations," in *Compass of the World*. Weigert, H. W. and Stefansson, V. (eds.). New York, The Macmillan Company, 1944, pp. 408–428.

————: "Genes as Physiological Agents," *American Naturalist*, 79: 289–303, 1945.

————: "On the Roles of Directed and Random Changes in Gene Frequency in the Genetics of Populations," *Evolution*, 2: 279–294, 1948.

————: "Population Structure in Evolution," *Proc. Am. Phil. Soc.*, 93: 471–478, 1950.

———— and DOBZHANSKY, TH.: "Genetics of National Populations, XII," *Genetics*, 31: 125–156, 1946.

"X": "The Sources of Soviet Conduct," *Foreign Affairs*, 25: 566–582, 1947.

YONGE, C. M.: "The Influence of Man on Marine Life," *Endeavour*, 6: 3–10, 1947.

YOUNG, J. Z.: "Giant Nerve-Fibres," *Endeavour*, 3: 108–113, 1944.

————: "The Functions of the Central Nervous System," *New Biology*, I, pp. 54–71. London, Penguin Books, 1946.

INDEX